Pharmacy Technician Certification Quick-Study Guide

4th Edition

NOTICE

The authors and publisher have made a conscientious effort to ensure that the information in this study guide is accurate and in accord with accepted standards at the time of publication. However, the information should be used solely for course work and preparation for the examination given by the Pharmacy Technician Certification Board. In no event should the information contained herein be used in connection with the actual services to be performed by pharmacy technicians.

This book is in no way authorized by or sponsored by the Pharmacy Technician Certification Board, Inc.

Drug therapy, other treatment, and pharmacy practice information are evolving constantly because of ongoing research and clinical experience, and they are often subject to interpretation. The publisher, editors, authors, reviewers, and other contributors have made every effort to ensure the accuracy and completeness of the information presented in this publication. However, these parties cannot be held responsible for the continued currency of the information, any inadvertent errors or omissions, or the application of this information, and shall have no liability to any person or entity with regard to claims, loss, or damage caused or alleged to be caused, directly or indirectly, by the use of information contained herein. Readers are advised that decisions regarding any treatment, including drug therapy, must be based on the independent judgment of the clinician, changing information about a treatment or drug (e.g., as reflected in the literature and manufacturer's most current product information), and changing medical practices.

Pharmacy Technician Certification Quick-Study Guide

4th Edition

Kristin W. Weitzel, PharmD, CDE, FAPhA
Clinical Associate Professor
University of Florida College of Pharmacy
Gainesville, Florida

William A. Hopkins Jr., PharmD, FACA
President
Clinical Pharmacy Consultants of North Georgia
Big Canoe, Georgia

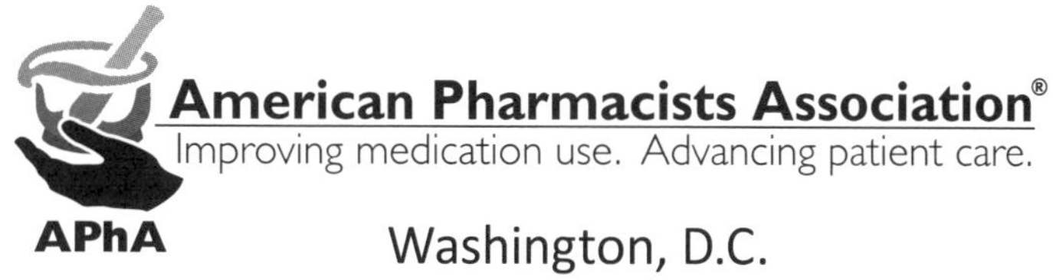

Washington, D.C.

Acquisitions Editor: Sandra J. Cannon
Managing Editor: Vicki Meade, Meade Communications
Copy Editor: Mary De Angelo
Proofreader: Betty Bruner
Design and Layout: Michele Danoff, Graphics by Design
Cover Designer: Mariam Safi

APhA was founded in 1852 as the American Pharmaceutical Association.

Published by the American Pharmacists Association
2215 Constitution Avenue, NW
Washington, D.C. 20037-2985
www.pharmacist.com
www.pharmacylibrary.com

To comment on this book via email, send your message to the publisher at aphabooks@aphanet.org

Library of Congress Cataloging-in-Publication Data

Weitzel, Kristin W., author.
Pharmacy technician certification : quick-study guide / Kristin W. Weitzel, William A. Hopkins Jr. -- Fourth edition.
p. ; cm. — (APhA pharmacy technician training series)
Preceded by: Pharmacy technician certification / Susan Moss Marks, William A. Hopkins, Jr. 3rd ed. 2006.
Includes bibliographical references and index.
ISBN 978-1-58212-188-8 (alk. paper)
I. Hopkins, William A., Jr. (William Alexander), 1947- author. II. Marks, Susan Moss. Pharmacy technician certification. Preceded by (work): III. American Pharmacists Association, issuing body. IV. Title. V. Series: APhA pharmacy technician training series.
[DNLM: 1. Pharmacy—Examination Questions. 2. Pharmacy--Outlines. 3. Pharmacists' Aides—Examination Questions. 4. Pharmacists' Aides--Outlines. QV 18.2]
RM301.13
615.1076--dc23
2013018352

How to Order This Book
Online: www.pharmacist.com/shop
By phone: 800-878-0729 (from the United States and Canada)
VISA®, MasterCard®, and American Express® cards accepted

This book is dedicated to Todd, Keegan, and Zack.
Thank you always for your love, understanding, and support.

Contents

Preface

Since the third edition of this book was published in 2006, the pharmacy technician profession has changed tremendously. Today, greater opportunities exist for pharmacy technicians in many practice settings. An increasing number of states now require registration or certification by national examination for pharmacy technician licensure or practice. Continuing education requirements to maintain an existing technician license are also becoming more closely regulated.

These and other professional changes impacted the Pharmacy Technician Certification Board (PTCB)'s February 2012 Job Analysis Study of more than 25,000 pharmacy technicians. This analysis led to a significant revision of the Pharmacy Technician Certification Exam (PTCE) blueprint—the method for distributing content areas throughout the 90-question examination. The updated blueprint, outlined in **Appendix A**, provides specific domain descriptions and a more detailed percentage breakdown of content areas than the previous version. The updated PTCE blueprint provided an excellent starting point for revising the *Pharmacy Technician Certification Quick-Study Guide*. Using the new blueprint as a guide, this fourth edition addresses the breadth of what the pharmacy technician needs to know in the most efficient way possible.

Every chapter in this edition has been completely revised to ensure that updated content is consistent with the new PTCE domains. As outlined in **Appendix B**, this revised edition covers every subject area on the exam. The book provides over 200 multiple-choice practice test questions presented in the same format as PTCE questions and includes nearly 250 pharmacy calculation questions with complete step-by-step answers in the **Answer Key**.

Nine new chapters have also been added, including information on commonly used medications and herbal products, laws and regulations impacting pharmacy technicians, sterile and nonsterile compounding, third-party billing systems, patient safety, pharmacy quality assurance, and inventory management. Each chapter retains the focused nature of previous editions to enable technicians to quickly identify exactly what they need to know.

Similar to the first edition, the updated *Pharmacy Technician Certification Quick-Study Guide* includes a comprehensive pharmacy calculations review. The practice problems are extensive and practical. Based on case scenarios and problems that pharmacy technicians will likely see in practice, the problems emphasize how to apply knowledge to practice in a real-world environment.

When you consider the important impact that a pharmacy technician has on the quality of patient care, the many changes in the pharmacy technician profession make sense. Technicians stand on the front lines in health systems, community pharmacies, and other practice settings across the nation. They work in partnership with pharmacists to help decrease medication errors, increase patient safety, and improve patient outcomes and satisfaction. I hope this revised and updated book helps technicians continue to grow and collaborate with pharmacists and patients to achieve these goals.

I'd like to thank Julian Graubart and Sandy Cannon at APhA for their assistance in making this revision a reality. I am also grateful to L. Michael Posey for his guidance in answering the many questions that came up along the way. I offer special thanks to Susan Moss Marks, who was a coauthor with William A. Hopkins Jr. on the first three editions of this book and played a pivotal role in making it a valuable tool for pharmacy technicians.

Kristin W. Weitzel
March 2013

Section I

Pharmacology for Technicians

Kristin W. Weitzel

Section I includes information related to medication terminology and commonly used medications, herbals, and dietary supplements, such as:

- definitions of commonly used drug and dosage terms
- an explanation of therapeutic equivalence
- commonly used brand and generic drug names, side effects, and interactions
- dosages and indications of frequently used drugs

Chapter 1

Medication Terminology

I. Key Terms and Concepts

A. Pharmacy technicians must understand medication terminology to ensure accuracy in selecting the appropriate drug product and in filling prescriptions and medication orders.

B. *Pharmacology* is the science that deals with the origin, nature, chemistry, effects, and uses of drugs.

C. The terms *trade* and *proprietary* refer to the manufacturer's brand name (protected by trademark) for a particular drug.

D. The terms *generic* and *nonproprietary* refer to a drug name not protected by a trademark, which is usually descriptive of its chemical structure.

E. Compounding is the act or process of combining two or more drug products or chemicals into a single preparation.

F. *Drug interactions* occur when one drug affects or is affected by another substance or condition in the body.

II. Understanding Drug Actions and Uses

A. Pharmacology and drug classifications

1. Technicians should be knowledgeable about drug actions and pharmacological classifications. **Chapter 2** details information about commonly used medications, herbals, and dietary supplements.

III. Strengths, Dosages, and Dosage Forms

A. Drugs are supplied commercially in various strengths and administered in different dosages.

1. The *strength* of a drug is the amount of drug contained in a specified unit.

2. The *dose* or *dosage* of a drug is the quantity of drug taken by a patient. The dose may be expressed as a "daily" dose, "single" dose, or even a "total" dose, which refers to the entire quantity of the drug taken throughout therapy. Daily doses may be given once daily, which is a single dose, or may be divided throughout the day.

    a. The strength is usually specific to the drug and the dosage is specific to the patient. For example, a patient may be prescribed hydrochlorothiazide tablets in a *strength* of 25 mg per tablet and instructed to take a *dosage* of one-half tablet daily (12.5 mg daily).

3. The *dosage form* (e.g., tablet, ointment) usually depends on the route of administration. The dosage form may also affect how quickly or slowly the drug is released into the body. **Table 1-1** lists common dosage forms.

TABLE 1-1. Common Dosage Forms

aerosol	enema	lozenge	solution
capsule	extract	ointment	suppository
cream	gel	paste	suspension
drops	granule	patch	syrup
elixir	injection	pellet or implant	tablet
emulsion	lotion	powder	tincture

4. The *dosage regimen* refers to the schedule of medication administration (e.g., every 4 hours, 3 times a day, at bedtime).

5. When a drug is not commercially available in a specific strength or dosage form, it may need to be compounded specially for a specific patient. **Section IV** includes more details about pharmacy compounding.

IV. Physical Appearance

A. Drugs have distinctive physical appearances, colors, odors, and textures.

1. A change in physical appearance may indicate a drug is expired, contaminated, or should no longer be used.

2. A drug's physical appearance can be verified in the package insert or with a print or online pharmacy reference.

V. Routes of Administration

The *route of administration* is the way the drug gets into the body (e.g., by mouth or injection). **Table 1-2** lists drug administration routes.

TABLE 1-2. Drug Administration Routes

buccal	intranasal	oral	sublingual
epidural	intraperitoneal	otic	topical
inhalation	intrathecal	parenteral	transdermal
intra-arterial	intravenous	perivascular	urethral
intracardiac	nasal	rectal	urogenital
intramuscular	ophthalmic	subcutaneous	vaginal

VI. Therapeutic Equivalence

A. The term *therapeutic equivalence* refers to the process that certifies that a generic drug has the same active ingredients, dosage form, standards for purity and quality, and standards for manufacturing, and that the same amount of drug is absorbed in the body over the same time as with the proprietary (brand name) drug.

B. The U.S. Food and Drug Administration's (FDA) *Orange Book* assigns therapeutic equivalence ratings to generic drugs. For example, "AB-rated" generic drugs are considered to be therapeutically equivalent to their brand counterparts.

VII. Drug Interactions

A. Drug interactions can cause additive or antagonistic effects, or potentiate the effects of one of the interacting drugs.

B. Different types of drug interactions include:

1. *Drug-Drug*: one drug (prescription or nonprescription) affects the action of another drug. For example, some antibiotics increase levels of the blood thinner warfarin by changing how warfarin is metabolized.

2. *Drug-Disease*: a patient's disease affects a drug's action or the drug worsens a patient's disease. For example, patients with uncontrolled high blood pressure should avoid oral pseudoephedrine decongestants because they may increase blood pressure.

3. *Drug-Dietary Supplement*: a dietary supplement interacts with the drug. For example, St. John's wort can decrease levels of some birth control pills.

4. *Drug-Laboratory*: a drug affects a patient's laboratory test, such as drugs that change urine color and affect urinalysis results.

5. *Drug-Nutrient*: a nutrient interacts with a drug or the drug affects nutrient levels, such as drugs that decrease levels of some vitamins.

C. Use caution when you see a drug interaction. Although some are benign, others can have serious effects and cause dangerously high or low drug levels. Pharmacy technicians should alert the pharmacist when a drug interaction is detected.

VIII. Chapter Summary

A. As health care practitioners involved daily with medications, technicians must understand all aspects of medication terminology. Familiarity with medical terms and their practical use can help technicians to accurately interpret drug orders and avoid medication errors.

B. When handling drug products or processing prescriptions and medication orders, technicians must ensure the appropriate medication strength, dosage, dosage form, and route of administration.

C. When substituting a generic medication for a proprietary medication, ensure that it is therapeutically equivalent to the brand name product.

D. Technicians should stay alert for drug interactions to help avoid drug therapy problems.

IX. Questions for Discussion

A. Discuss the difference between a drug's strength and its dosage.

B. Why is it important to examine a drug's physical appearance when filling a prescription?

C. Discuss some examples of non-oral drug administration routes. When might these be used in practice?

D. What factors should you evaluate when determining the therapeutic equivalence of two drugs? What could result if a generic drug is administered that is not equivalent to its proprietary counterpart?

E. Why is it important to look for drug interactions when processing prescription orders? List some examples of potentially harmful drug interactions.

X. Sample Questions

1. A prescription is written for amoxicillin 500 mg, Take 2 capsules (1000 mg) daily. What is the strength of the amoxicillin in this prescription?

   a. 500 mg
   b. 1000 mg
   c. 1500 mg
   d. 2000 mg

2. A drug's brand name is also referred to as which of the following:

   a. nonproprietary name
   b. trade name
   c. marked name
   d. FDA name

3. Which of the following terms describes a dosage form?

   a. suppository
   b. intravenous
   c. lozenge
   d. both a and c

4. Which of the following terms describes a route of administration?

   a. intranasal
   b. proprietary
   c. dosage form
   d. nutrient

5. A brand and generic drug are tested to determine if they have the same active ingredients, dosage form, standards for purity and quality, and standards for manufacturing. This process is called determining:

   a. proprietary natures
   b. drug sameness
   c. therapeutic equivalence
   d. dosage forms

6. A patient takes two drugs that have additive effects causing excessive drowsiness. This is an example of which of the following types of drug interactions:

   a. drug-drug
   b. drug-nutrient
   c. drug-dietary supplement
   d. drug-laboratory

7. While entering a prescription into the computer, you see an alert about a potential interaction between a patient's warfarin and his ginkgo biloba. This is an example of which of the following types of interactions:

   a. drug-drug
   b. drug-nutrient
   c. drug-dietary supplement
   d. drug-laboratory

The **Answer Key** appears in **Section VIII**.

Notes:

Chapter 2

Commonly Used Medications, Herbals, and Dietary Supplements

I. Key Terms and Concepts

A. A drug's *indication* or use is the reason the agent is prescribed for a patient or the purpose of a drug's use for self treatment.

B. An *adverse effect* is a harmful or undesirable effect caused by administration of a medication.

C. *Drug allergies* occur when the body's immune system reacts to a drug.

D. A *contraindication* is a reason why a specific drug either cannot be used or should be used only with caution in a specific patient population.

II. Pharmacology

A. A drug's *indication* or use is a valid reason the agent is prescribed for a patient or the purpose of a drug's use for self treatment. An indication may be approved by the U.S. Food and Drug Administration (FDA) or a drug can be used "off-label" for a specific purpose without FDA approval.

B. An *adverse effect* is a harmful or undesirable effect caused by administration of a medication. Adverse effects may be local or systemic. Adverse effects are listed below for commonly used drug classes.

1. *Central nervous system* medications include antidepressants, antipsychotics, anxiety medications, medications for Parkinson's disease and Alzheimer's disease, antiseizure and antimigraine agents, drugs to treat attention deficit and hyperactivity disorder, and centrally acting pain medications.
   Common adverse effects: dizziness, sleepiness, changes in heart rate or breathing, confusion, drowsiness, nausea, dry mouth, insomnia, nervousness, weight changes, extrapyramidal symptoms, changes in blood pressure, and restlessness.

2. *Respiratory* medications include inhaled corticosteroids, inhaled beta-agonists, medications for asthma, and medications for chronic obstructive pulmonary disease.
   Common adverse effects: tremor, fast heart rate, sore throat, and oral fungal infection or throat irritation.

3. *Gastrointestinal* medications include acid-reducing medications such as proton pump inhibitors and immune modulating drugs such as infliximab.
   Common adverse effects: headache, dizziness, rash, and infusion-related reactions.

4. *Endocrine* agents include diabetes and thyroid medications and corticosteroids (prednisone, etc.).
   Common adverse effects: low blood sugar, weight or appetite changes, nausea/vomiting, and stomach upset.

5. *Hormonal* agents include estrogens, progestins, and testosterone.
   Common adverse effects: headache, dizziness, nausea, changes in vaginal bleeding patterns, fluid retention, and changes in mood or appetite.

6. *Cardiac medications that affect blood pressure* include angiotensin-converting enzyme (ACE) inhibitors, angiotensin receptor blockers, calcium channel blockers, beta-blockers, and diuretics.
   Common adverse effects: dizziness, cough, low blood pressure, swelling of the feet or ankles, slow heart rate, drowsiness, and changes in potassium, sodium, or other electrolyte levels.

7. *Cardiac medications that modify lipid levels* include statins, ezetimibe, niacin, fenofibrate, and gemfibrozil.
   Common adverse effects: flatulence, nausea, muscle pain, and upset stomach.

8. *Cardiac anti-clotting medications* include aspirin, warfarin, heparin, low-molecular weight heparins, newer anticoagulants (dabigatran, rivaroxaban, etc.).
   Common adverse effect: bleeding.

9. *Genitourinary* agents include drugs for overactive bladder, erectile dysfunction, and prostate enlargement.
   Common adverse effects: changes in libido, upset stomach, headache, dry mouth, and flushing.

C. *Drug allergies* occur when the body's immune system reacts to a drug. Drug allergies can cause minor skin reactions, such as rash or hives, or a more serious reaction such as swelling of the throat and difficulty breathing (anaphylaxis). As detailed in **Chapter 6**, drug allergy information should be verified and updated at each new prescription or refill.

D. A *contraindication* (also called therapeutic contraindication or warning) is a reason why a specific drug either cannot be used or should be used only with caution in a specific patient population or in patients with an existing condition. Contraindications are included in the prescribing information for every approved drug.

E. Pharmacy technicians should stay up to date on the most frequent uses, warnings, and adverse effects of commonly used medications.

III. Commonly Used Medications: Selected from Community and Hospital Settings

Generic Name	Brand Name	General Use(s)	Usual Dosage Range*
Abacavir/Lamivudine	Epzicom	HIV infection	1 tablet (abacavir 600 mg/lamivudine 300 mg) once daily
Abobotulinumtoxin A	Dysport	Cervical dystonia, facial wrinkles	Dosage varies based on indication and patient-specific factors
Adapalene	Differin	Acne	Apply to affected areas in the evening before bed
Albuterol (inhaler)	Proventil HFA, Pro-Air HFA, Ventolin HFA	Bronchospasm	180 micrograms (2 puffs) inhaled every 4 to 6 hours as needed
Albuterol/Ipratropium (inhaler)	Combivent	COPD	2 puffs inhaled 4 times daily
Alprazolam	Xanax	Anxiety	0.25 mg to 0.5 mg by mouth three times daily, titrated up to 4 mg daily in divided doses
Alteplase	Activase	Dissolves blood clots in MI, stroke, pulmonary embolism, catheter occlusion	100 mg IV, depending on indication
Amlodipine	Norvasc	Angina, hypertension	5 to 10 mg by mouth once daily
Amlodipine/Valsartan	Exforge	Hypertension	1 tablet (amlodipine 5 mg/valsartan 160 mg) by mouth daily initially; increase as needed
Aripiprazole	Abilify	Psychotic disorders	15 mg daily by mouth
Atomoxetine	Strattera	ADHD	40 to 100 mg by mouth daily
Aspirin/Dipyridamole	Aggrenox	Reduce stroke risk	1 capsule (dipyridamole 200 mg/aspirin 25 mg) by mouth twice daily
Atazanavir	Reyataz	HIV infection	300 mg by mouth once daily
Atorvastatin	Lipitor	High cholesterol, lower stroke or MI risk	10 to 80 mg by mouth once daily
Azelastine (nasal spray)	Astelin	Allergies	1 to 2 sprays per nostril twice daily
Azithromycin	Zithromax	Bacterial infections	500 mg by mouth on the first day followed by 250 mg daily for 4 days (Z-pak)
Beclomethasone (inhaler)	Qvar	Asthma (chronic)	40 to 160 mcg inhaled twice daily
Bevacizumab	Avastin	Metastatic colorectal cancer	5 or 10 mg/kg given intravenously every 14 days
Bimatoprost (ophthalmic solution)	Lumigan	Ocular hypertension, open-angle glaucoma	1 drop in affected eye(s) once daily in the evening
Bivalirudin	Angiomax	Prevention of clotting in angina/PTCA	0.75 mg/kg by IV bolus followed by 1.75 mg/kg/hour IV infusion
Brimonidine (ophthalmic solution)	Alphagan P	Glaucoma/ocular hypertension	1 drop in affected eye(s) 3 times daily

continued

Generic Name	Brand Name	General Use(s)	Usual Dosage Range*
Budesonide (nasal spray)	Rhinocort Aqua	Allergies	1 spray per nostril once daily in the morning
Budesonide/Formoterol	Symbicort	Asthma, COPD	2 inhalations twice daily
Buprenorphine/Naloxone	Suboxone	Opioid dependence	16 mg/4 mg buprenorphine and naloxone sublingually once daily (target dose)
Bupropion (extended/sustained release)	Wellbutrin XL, Budeprion SR	Depression, seasonal affective disorder	150 mg to 300 mg by mouth once daily
Capecitabine	Xeloda	Breast cancer	Dosage varies based on indication and patient-specific factors
Ceftriaxone	Rocephin	Bacterial infections	1 to 2 g IV or IM every 24 hours, depending on the severity of the infection and organism susceptibility
Celecoxib	Celebrex	Osteoarthritis, rheumatoid arthritis, acute pain	200 mg by mouth once daily or 100 mg by mouth twice daily
Cephalexin	Keflex	Bacterial infections	500 mg by mouth every 12 hours for common infections
Cetuximab	Erbitux	Various cancers	Dosage varies based on indication and patient-specific factors
Cinacalcet	Sensipar	Secondary hyperparathyroidism, hypercalcemia in parathyroid cancer	30 mg by mouth twice daily up to 90 mg 3 to 4 times daily
Ciprofloxacin/dexamethasone (otic)	Ciprodex	Acute otitis media	4 drops instilled into the affected ear twice daily for 7 days
Clarithromycin (extended release)	Biaxin XL	Bacterial infections	1000 mg (two 500 mg tablets) by mouth once daily for common infections
Clonidine (transdermal)	Catapres-TTS	Hypertension	1 patch applied every 7 days
Clopidogrel	Plavix	Reduce stroke, MI risk, acute coronary syndrome	75 mg by mouth once daily
Colchicine	Colcrys	Gout	0.6 mg by mouth once to twice daily
Cyclosporine (ocular)	Restasis	Increase tear production	1 drop in affected eye(s) twice daily
Dabigatran	Pradaxa	Reduce risk of stroke	150 mg by mouth twice daily
Dalteparin	Fragmin	Blood clot prevention and treatment, angina	120 IU/kg (max: 10,000 IU) SC every 12 hours
Daptomycin	Cubicin	Bacterial infections	4 to 6 mg/kg IV once daily
Darbepoetin alfa	Aranesp	Anemia	0.45 mcg/kg SC or IV once weekly or 0.75 mcg/kg IV or SC once every 2 weeks
Darunavir	Prezista	HIV infection	800 mg (given with ritonavir 100 mg) by mouth once daily with food
Desvenlafaxine	Pristiq	Depression	50 mg by mouth once daily
Dexlansoprazole	Dexilant	Erosive esophagitis, GERD	30 mg by mouth once daily

Generic Name	Brand Name	General Use(s)	Usual Dosage Range*
Dexmethylphenidate	Focalin XR	ADHD	10 to 40 mg by mouth once daily in the morning
Dextroamphetamine/ Amphetamine (extended release)	Adderall XR	ADHD	10 to 20 mg by mouth once daily in the morning
Diclofenac (gel)	Voltaren Gel	Osteoarthritis (knee, hand)	4 g for each knee, ankle, or foot four times daily
Digoxin	Digitek, Lanoxin	CHF, atrial fibrillation	Doses vary; 3.4 to 5.1 mcg/kg/day by mouth once daily (recommended starting maintenance dose)
Diltiazem	Tiazac, Taztia XT	Hypertension, angina	120 to 360 mg by mouth once daily
Donepezil	Aricept	Alzheimer's disease	5 to 10 mg by mouth daily
Dorzolamide/Timolol	Cosopt	Glaucoma/ocular hypertension	1 drop in affected eye(s) twice daily
Duloxetine	Cymbalta	Anxiety, depression, fibromyalgia	40 to 60 mg/day by mouth in 1 or 2 divided doses
Dutasteride	Avodart	Benign prostatic hypertrophy (BPH)	0.5 mg by mouth once daily
Eletriptan	Relpax	Migraines	20 or 40 mg by mouth as a single dose; may repeat once after at least 2 hours
Enoxaparin sodium	Lovenox	Prevention of blood clots	20 mg SC once daily
Epoetin alfa	Epogen, Procrit	Anemia	50 to 100 units/kg IV/SC three times a week
Escitalopram	Lexapro	Depression, anxiety	10 to 20 mg by mouth once daily
Esomeprazole	Nexium	GERD, erosive esophagitis	20 mg by mouth once daily, taken 1 hour before meals
Estradiol (transdermal)	Vivelle-Dot, Climara	Estrogen replacement	1 patch applied to trunk or buttocks; replace twice weekly
Estrogens, conjugated	Premarin, Cenestin	Estrogen replacement	0.3 to 0.625 mg by mouth once daily
Estrogens, conjugated/ Medroxyprogesterone	Prempro	Estrogen replacement	1 tablet by mouth once daily
Eszopiclone	Lunesta	Insomnia	2 to 3 mg by mouth immediately before retiring
Etanercept	Enbrel	Rheumatoid/psoriatic arthritis	50 mg/week SC given either once or twice weekly
Ethinyl estradiol/Desogestrel	Apri, Mircette, Kariva	Contraception	1 tablet by mouth once daily for 21 days, followed by 7 days without drug
Ethinyl estradiol/Drospirenone	Yasmin, Yaz	Contraception	1 tablet by mouth once daily for 21 days (Yasmin) or 24 days (Yaz), followed by remainder of 28-day cycle without drug
Ethinyl estradiol/Ethynodiol	Zovia 1/35E	Contraception	1 tablet by mouth once daily for 21 days, followed by 7 days without drug

continued

Generic Name	Brand Name	General Use(s)	Usual Dosage Range*
Ethinyl estradiol/Etonogestrel	NuvaRing	Contraception	Insert 1 ring on or before Day 5 of cycle; remove ring after 3 weeks, followed by a one-week rest
Ethinyl estradiol/Levonorgestrel	Aviane, Alesse, Levora, Triphasil, Trivora-28	Contraception	1 tablet by mouth once daily for 21 days, followed by 7 days without drug
Ethinyl estradiol/ Norelgestromin (transdermal)	Ortho Evra	Contraception	1 transdermal system applied topically; remove and reapply once weekly for 3 weeks, followed by a patch-free period of 1 week
Ethinyl estradiol/Norgestimate	Sprintec, Ortho-Cyclen, Ortho Tri-Cyclen	Contraception	1 tablet by mouth once daily for 21 days, followed by 7 days without drug
Exenatide	Byetta, Bydureon	Diabetes	5 mcg SC twice a day within the 60 minutes before morning and evening meal (Byetta); 2 mg SC once every 7 days (Bydureon)
Ezetimibe	Zetia	Hyperlipidemia	10 mg by mouth once daily
Ezetimibe/Simvastatin	Vytorin	Hypercholesterolemia	Ezetimibe/simvastatin 10/10 mg to 10/40 mg once daily in the evening
Fenofibrate	Tricor	Hyperlipidemia	48 to 145 mg by mouth once daily
Fenofibric acid	Trilipix	Hyperlipidemia	135 mg by mouth once daily
Finasteride	Proscar, Propecia	Benign prostatic hypertrophy, male pattern baldness	5 mg by mouth once daily
Fluoxetine	Prozac	Depression, bulimia, OCD	20 to 80 mg by mouth daily
Fluticasone (inhaler)	Flovent HFA	Asthma	440 mcg via oral inhalation twice daily
Fluticasone (nasal)	Flonase, Veramyst	Allergies	2 sprays per nostril once daily
Fluticasone/Salmeterol (inhaler)	Advair Diskus	Asthma (chronic), COPD	1 inhalation twice daily
Fluvastatin (extended release)	Lescol XL	Hyperlipidemia, secondary prevention of heart disease	20 to 80 mg by mouth once daily
Gabapentin	Neurontin	Seizures, postherpetic neuralgia	300 to 3600 mg by mouth daily
Gatifloxacin (ocular)	Zymar	Ocular infections	1 drop in each affected eye every 2 hours while awake (days 1 and 2), then 1 drop in each affected eye up to 4 times daily (days 3 to 7)
Glimepiride	Amaryl	Type 2 diabetes	1 to 4 mg once daily
Ibandronate	Boniva	Postmenopausal osteo-porosis	2.5 mg by mouth once daily or 150 mg by mouth once monthly
Imatinib	Gleevec	Chronic myeloid leukemia, gastrointestinal stromal tumors	Dosage varies based on indication and patient-specific factors

Generic Name	Brand Name	General Use(s)	Usual Dosage Range*
Infliximab	Remicade	Crohn's disease, arthritis syndromes, ulcerative colitis, psoriasis, psoriatic arthritis	Dosage varies based on indication and patient-specific factors
Insulin, aspart	Novolog	Diabetes	Insulin doses are individualized to achieve blood glucose control
Insulin, detemir	Levemir	Diabetes	Insulin doses are individualized to achieve blood glucose control
Insulin, glargine	Lantus	Diabetes	Insulin doses are individualized to achieve blood glucose control
Insulin, lispro	Humalog	Diabetes	Insulin doses are individualized to achieve blood glucose control
Ipilimumab	Yervoy	Metastatic melanoma	Dosage varies based on indication and patient-specific factors
Irbesartan	Avapro	Hypertension, diabetic nephropathy	150 mg by mouth once daily
Lamotrigine	Lamictal, Lamictal CD, Lamictal XR, others	Seizures, bipolar disorder	25 to 500 mg by mouth daily given in single or divided doses (dosing frequency dependent on indication and dosage form)
Lansoprazole	Prevacid	GERD, duodenal ulcer	15 to 30 mg by mouth once daily in the morning
Latanoprost (ophthalmic solution)	Xalatan	Glaucoma, ocular hypertension	1 drop (1.5 mcg) in affected eye(s) once daily in the evening
Levalbuterol (solution or suspension for inhalation)	Xopenex, Xopenex HFA	Bronchospasm	90 mcg (2 inhalations) every 4 to 6 hours (Xopenex HFA), starting dose of 0.63 mg inhaled by nebulization three times per day (Xopenex nebulizer solution)
Levetiracetam	Keppra	Partial seizures	1000 to 3000 mg daily in divided doses
Levofloxacin	Levaquin	Bacterial infections	250 to 750 mg by mouth or IV every 24 hours
Levothyroxine	Synthroid, Levoxyl, Levothroid	Hypothyroidism	Usual replacement dose is 1.7 mcg/kg by mouth daily
Lidocaine (transdermal)	Lidoderm	Postherpetic neuralgia (PHN)	Up to 3 patches applied to cover most painful area for up to 12 hours in a 24-hour period
Linezolid	Zyvox	Vancomycin-resistant bacterial infections	600 mg by mouth or IV every 12 hours
Liraglutide	Victoza	Type 2 diabetes	1.2 to 1.8 mg SC once daily
Lisdexamfetamine dimesylate	Vyvanse	ADHD	30 to 70 mg by mouth once daily in the morning
Lopinavir/Ritonavir	Kaletra	HIV infection	400 mg lopinavir; 100 mg ritonavir by mouth twice daily

continued

Generic Name	Brand Name	General Use(s)	Usual Dosage Range*
Losartan	Cozaar	Hypertension	50 to 100 mg/day by mouth, given in 1 to 2 divided doses
Losartan/HCTZ	Hyzaar	Hypertension	50 to 100 mg/day losartan; 12.5 to 25 mg/day HCTZ
Memantine	Namenda	Alzheimer's disease	10 mg by mouth twice daily
Mesalamine	Asacol, Lialda, Pentasa, others	Inflammatory bowel disease	2.4 g or 4.8 g by mouth in single or divided doses given three times per day, depending on dosage form (also available in rectal form)
Methotrexate	Rheumatrex, Trexall	Cancer, rheumatoid arthritis	Usual dose is 7.5 to 15 mg by mouth once weekly for rheumatoid arthritis; cancer dosing varies
Methylphenidate	Concerta, Methylin, others	ADHD, narcolepsy	Dose varies based on dosage form; usual dose range is 10 to 60 mg/day
Metoprolol (extended release)	Toprol-XL	Hypertension, angina, MI	25 to 100 mg by mouth once daily
Metronidazole	Flagyl	Bacterial infections	1 to 2 grams in single or divided doses, with dosing frequency dependent on indication
Minocycline	Solodyn	Acne	1 mg/kg by mouth once daily
Modafinil	Provigil	Narcolepsy, sleep disorders	200 mg by mouth once daily in the morning
Mometasone (nasal)	Nasonex	Allergies	2 sprays (50 mcg/spray) in each nostril once daily
Montelukast	Singulair	Asthma, seasonal allergies	10 mg by mouth once daily in the evening
Morphine sulfate	Morphine sulfate	Pain	Dose varies based on pain severity and patient-specific factors
Moxifloxacin	Avelox	Bacterial infections	400 mg by mouth or IV once daily
Moxifloxacin (ocular)	Vigamox	Bacterial conjunctivitis	1 drop in affected eye(s) three times per day
Mupirocin (topical)	Bactroban	Impetigo, skin infection	A small amount applied to affected area 3 times daily
Niacin	Niaspan	Hyperlipidemia	1.5 to 3 g/day by mouth, given in 2 to 3 divided doses
Nitroglycerin (sublingual)	NitroQuick, Nitrostat, Nitrolingual, Nitrotab	Angina	1 tablet SL dissolved under the tongue or in buccal pouch immediately following chest pain
Nitroglycerin (transdermal)	Minitran, Nitro-Dur, Transderm-Nitro, Deponit	Angina	1 transdermal dosing system applied topically to intact skin every 24 hours
Ofloxacin (Otic)	Floxin Otic	Otitis externa	10 drops instilled into affected ear once daily for 7 days
Olanzapine/Fluoxetine	Symbyax	Bipolar disorder/ depression	Olanzapine 6 to 18 mg/fluoxetine 25 to 50 mg once daily

Generic Name	Brand Name	General Use(s)	Usual Dosage Range*
Olmesartan	Benicar	Hypertension	20 to 40 mg/day by mouth once daily
Olmesartan/HCTZ	Benicar HCT	Hypertension	10 to 40 mg olmesartan/12.5 to 25 mg HCTZ once daily
Olopatadine (ophthalmic solution)	Patanol	Allergic conjunctivitis	1 drop in affected eye(s) two times per day at an interval of 6 to 8 hours
Omalizumab	Xolair	Asthma	150 to 375 mg SC every 2 or 4 weeks
Omega-3 acid ethyl esters	Lovaza	Hypertriglyceridemia	4 g/day by mouth in single or divided doses
OnabotulinumtoxinA	Botox, Botox Cosmetic	Cervical dystonia, severe underarm sweating, strabismus, eyelid tics, facial wrinkles, chronic migraine headaches, overactive bladder	Dose varies based on indication and patient-specific factors
Oxaliplatin	Eloxatin	Colon or rectal cancer (metastatic)	Use prescribed 2-day dose regimen; repeat every 2 weeks or as directed
Oxcarbazepine	Trileptal	Partial seizures (children)	600 to 2400 mg daily in divided doses
Oxycodone	OxyContin	Pain	Dose varies based on pain severity and patient-specific factors
Oxycodone/Acetaminophen	Endocet, Roxicet	Pain	Dose varies based on pain severity and patient-specific factors
Oxymorphone	Opana ER	Pain	Dose varies based on pain severity and patient-specific factors
Paclitaxel	Taxol	Various cancers	Dose varies based on type of cancer treated and patient-specific factors
Palonosetron	Aloxi	Nausea/vomiting	0.25 mg IV over 30 seconds given as a single dose 30 minutes prior to chemotherapy
Pantoprazole	Protonix	GERD, erosive esophagitis	20 to 40 mg by mouth once daily
Paroxetine (controlled release)	Paxil CR	Depression, OCD, panic disorder, social anxiety, post-traumatic stress disorder	12.5 to 62.5 mg per day
Pioglitazone	Actos	Type 2 diabetes	15 mg to 45 mg by mouth once daily
Piperacillin/Tazobactam	Zosyn	Bacterial infections	3.375 to 4.5 g IV every 6 hours for most infections
Potassium chloride	Klor-Con, Micro-K, others	Potassium replacement	Dosage varies based on patient-specific factors
Pregabalin	Lyrica	Seizures, fibromyalgia, diabetic neuropathy	150 to 300 mg daily in divided doses
Quetiapine	Seroquel	Psychotic disorders	100 to 800 mg daily in divided doses

continued

Generic Name	Brand Name	General Use(s)	Usual Dosage Range*
Rabeprazole	Aciphex	GERD, duodenal ulcer, hypersecretory disorders	20 mg by mouth once daily
Raloxifene	Evista	Osteoporosis prevention	60 mg by mouth once daily
Raltegravir	Isentress	HIV infection	400 mg by mouth twice daily with or without food
Ramipril	Altace	Hypertension, heart failure	10 mg/day by mouth given in 1 to 2 divided doses
Ranibizumab	Lucentis	Wet macular degeneration	0.5 mg (0.05 mL) monthly by intra-vitreal injection into affected eye
Ranolazine	Ranexa	Chronic angina	500 to 1000 mg by mouth twice daily
Repaglinide	Prandin	Type 2 diabetes	0.5 to 4 mg by mouth before meals up to 4 times daily
Rifaximin	Xifaxan	Traveler's diarrhea, hepatic encephalopathy	600 to 800 mg daily in divided doses
Risedronate	Actonel	Osteoporosis, Paget's disease	5 mg by mouth once daily or 35 mg once weekly or 150 mg per month
Risperidone	Risperdal	Psychotic disorders	1 to 6 mg/day by mouth
Rituximab	Rituxan	Rheumatoid arthritis, non-Hodgkin's lymphoma (NHL)	Dosage varies based on indication and patient-specific factors
Rivaroxaban	Xarelto	Preventive therapy for blood clots	10 to 30 mg by mouth daily given in single or divided doses
Rivastigmine	Exelon	Alzheimer's disease, Parkinson's dementia	1.5 to 3 mg by mouth twice daily
Rizatriptan	Maxalt, Maxalt-MLT	Migraines	5 to 10 mg by mouth as a single dose at migraine onset. May repeat once after 2 hours.
Ropinirole	Requip, Requip XL	Parkinson's disease, restless leg syndrome	2 to 24 mg by mouth daily given in single or divided doses
Salmeterol (inhalation)	Serevent Diskus	Asthma, COPD, broncho-spasm	50 mcg (1 oral inhalation) twice daily
Saxagliptin	Onglyza	Type 2 diabetes	2.5 to 5 mg by mouth once daily
Sertraline	Zoloft	Depression, social anxiety, OCD	50 to 200 mg by mouth once daily
Sildenafil	Viagra	ED	50 mg by mouth, approximately 1 hour before sexual activity, up to once daily
Simvastatin	Zocor	Hyperlipidemia, coronary heart disease	Usual dose is 5 to 40 mg by mouth once daily
Sitagliptin	Januvia	Type 2 diabetes	100 mg by mouth once daily
Sitagliptin/Metformin	Janumet	Type 2 diabetes	50 to 100 mg sitagliptin/1000 to 2000 mg metformin daily in divided doses
Solifenacin succinate	VESIcare	Overactive bladder	5 mg by mouth once daily

Generic Name	Brand Name	General Use(s)	Usual Dosage Range*
Tacrolimus	Prograf	Prevent organ transplant rejection	Dosage varies based on indication and patient-specific factors
Tadalafil	Cialis	ED	5 to 20 mg by mouth taken prior to anticipated sexual activity
Tamsulosin	Flomax	Benign prostatic hypertrophy	0.4 to 0.8 mg by mouth once daily
Telaprevir	Incivek	Chronic hepatitis C	750 mg by mouth 3 times daily
Tenofovir	Viread	HIV infection	300 mg by mouth once daily with or without food
Teriparatide	Forteo	Postmenopausal-related osteoporosis	20 mcg SC once daily
Testosterone (topical)	Androgel	Replacement therapy (men)	5 to 10 g of 1% gel applied once daily
Tiotropium bromide	Spiriva	COPD	18 mcg once daily via oral inhalation
Tobramycin/Dexamethasone (ophthalmic suspension)	TobraDex	Ocular infection and inflammation	1 to 2 drops suspension into conjunctival sac of affected eye(s) every 4 to 6 hours
Tolterodine (long acting)	Detrol LA	Bladder instability	2 to 4 mg by mouth once daily
Topiramate	Topamax	Seizures	25 to 400 mg by mouth daily given in divided doses
Tramadol	Ultram ER, Ultram	Pain	50 to 100 mg by mouth every 4 to 6 hours as needed
Tramadol/Acetaminophen	Ultracet	Short-term treatment of pain	2 tablets (37.5 mg tramadol and 325 mg acetaminophen per tablet) by mouth every 4 to 6 hours as needed
Trastuzumab	Herceptin	Breast cancer	Dosage varies based on indication and patient-specific factors
Travoprost (ocular)	Travatan	Open-angle glaucoma, ocular hypertension	1 drop in affected eye(s) once daily in the evening
Triamcinolone (nasal spray)	Nasacort AQ	Allergies	2 to 4 sprays in each nostril once daily
Valganciclovir	Valcyte	Cytomegalovirus retinitis in HIV patients	900 mg by mouth twice daily for 21 days
Valproic acid (extended release)	Depakote, Depakote ER	Seizures, bipolar disorder	10 to 60 mg/kg/day by mouth administered in divided doses 2 to 3 times per day (seizures)
Valsartan	Diovan	Hypertension, CHF	80 to 320 mg/day by mouth in single or divided doses
Valsartan/HCTZ	Diovan HCT	Hypertension	160 to 320 mg valsartan/12.5 to 25 mg HCTZ by mouth once daily
Vardenafil	Levitra	ED	5 to 20 mg by mouth approximately 60 minutes before sexual activity

continued

Generic Name	Brand Name	General Use(s)	Usual Dosage Range*
Varenicline	Chantix	Smoking cessation	0.5 to 2 mg by mouth given in single or divided doses 2 times daily
Venlafaxine (extended release)	Effexor XR	Depression, social anxiety disorder, panic disorder	75 to 225 mg by mouth once daily
Verapamil (sustained release)	Calan SR, Verelan PM, Isoptin SR, others	Angina, hypertension	180 to 480 mg by mouth in single or divided doses, with frequency dependent on indication and dosage form
Warfarin	Coumadin	Preventive therapy for blood clots	Dosage varies based on indication and patient-specific factors
Zaleplon	Sonata	Insomnia	10 mg by mouth at bedtime
Ziprasidone	Geodon	Schizophrenia, bipolar mania	20 to 80 mg by mouth twice daily
Zoledronic acid	Zometa	Hypercalcemia related to cancer, osteoporosis, Paget's disease	4 mg IV over a minimum of 15 minutes
Zolpidem	Ambien CR, Ambien, others	Insomnia	5 mg (females) or 5 to 10 mg (males) by mouth immediately before bedtime (Ambien), 6.25 mg (females) or 6.25 to 12.5 mg (males) by mouth immediately before bedtime (Ambien CR)
Zoster vaccine	Zostavax	Prevention of zoster (shingles)	0.65 mL/dose SC one time

*Dose ranges are for adults unless otherwise noted and are provided for test preparation purposes only for commonly used dosage forms/preparations. This chart is not intended to serve as a comprehensive dosing reference or to guide dosing decisions. Approved doses are subject to change, and all doses should be individualized based on indication and patient-specific factors. Pharmacy technicians should consult a drug information reference, the complete prescribing information, or another updated source for current dosing information in practice.

Abbreviations:

ADHD = attention-deficit hyperactivity disorder
BPH = benign prostatic hypertrophy
CHF = congestive heart failure
COPD = chronic obstructive pulmonary disease
ED = erectile dysfunction
GERD = gastroesophageal reflux disease
HCTZ = hydrochlorothiazide
HIV = human immunodeficiency virus
IM = intramuscular
IV = intravenous
MI = myocardial infarction
NHL = non-Hodgkin's lymphoma
OCD = obsessive-compulsive disorder
PHN = postherpetic neuralgia
PTCA= percutaneous transluminal coronary angioplasty
SC = subcutaneous
SL = sublingual

IV. Commonly Used Herbal Supplements

Herbal Product*	May also be called:	Has been used for:[+]
Alfalfa	*Medicago sativa*, clover, buffalo herb	Heart disease, diabetes, high cholesterol
Aloe vera	*Aloe vera*	Constipation, skin conditions, diabetes, wound healing
Bilberry	*Vaccinium myrtillus*, resveratrol, wineberry, blueberry	Heart disease, diabetes, cataracts, diarrhea, dysmenorrhea, breast disease, glaucoma, peptic ulcer disease, retinopathy
Black cohosh	*Actaea racemosa*, Remifemin®	Menopausal symptoms, infertility, pain, breast cancer, migraine
Cayenne	*Capsicum annuum*, capsaicin	Pain, nausea/vomiting, dyspepsia/ulcer, sore throat/cold symptoms, weight loss, ear infections
Cranberry	*Vaccinium macrocarpon*, anthocyanins, dried cranberries, Azo cranberry®	Prevention of urinary tract infection, *H. pylori* infection, dental plaque, and cancer; memory enhancement, heart disease, diabetes
Dandelion	*Taraxacum* spp., asteraceae	Inflammation, anticancer, colitis, diabetes, gastrointestinal disorders
Echinacea	*Echinacea* spp.	Prevention and treatment of the common cold, immune system stimulation, vaginal yeast infections, cancer, ear infections
Elderberry	*Sambucus nigra*, elder flower	Influenza, sinus and respiratory infections, high cholesterol
Evening primrose oil	*Oenothera biennis*, EPO, gamma-linolenic acid, linoleic acid	Atopic dermatitis and eczema, diabetes, cancer, obesity, arthritis, osteoporosis, breast pain, bronchitis
Garlic	*Allium sativum*, allicin	High cholesterol, hypertension, heart disease, antibacterial and antifungal properties, cancer, gastritis, infections, diabetes, warts
Ginger	*Zingiber officinale*, ginger root	Nausea/vomiting, motion sickness, pain, anti-platelet effects, high cholesterol
Ginkgo	*Ginkgo biloba*	Claudication (vascular disease), dementia, memory impairment, asthma, heart disease, depression, premenstrual syndrome, vertigo/dizziness
Ginseng	*Panax ginseng*, American ginseng, Asian ginseng	Diabetes, immune system enhancement, mental performance, Alzheimer's disease, cancer, heart disease, infections, pain
Grape seed	*Vitis vinifera*, bioflavinols, grape seed extract or oil, pycnogenol	Antioxidant/heart protection, chronic venous insufficiency, edema, diabetic retinopathy, high cholesterol, skin protection
Green tea	*Camellia sinensis*	Genital warts, allergies, anxiety, cancer, heart disease, common cold prevention, diabetes, high cholesterol, menopause, obesity
Hawthorn	*Crataegus* spp.	Heart failure or heart disease, anxiety, hypertension
Horny goat weed	*Epimedium* spp.	Atherosclerosis, sexual dysfunction
Horse chestnut	*Aesculus hippocastanum*, Spanish chestnut	Chronic venous insufficiency
Kava kava	*Piper methysticum*, kava, kawa	Anxiety, insomnia, Parkinson's disease, stress
Kelp	Alginic acid, seaweed, bladderwrack	Weight loss, antibacterial/antifungal, blood thinner, cancer, thyroid disease, diabetes

continued

Herbal Product*	May also be called:	Has been used for:⁺
Milk thistle	*Silybum marianum*, wild artichoke	Cirrhosis, liver disease, cancer, dyspepsia, high cholesterol, menopausal symptoms
Olive leaf	*Olea europaea*	Antibacterial, antifungal, or antioxidant properties
Red clover	*Trifolium pratense*, cow clover, wild clover, isoflavone clover extract	Hormone replacement, menopausal symptoms, osteoporosis, high cholesterol
Saw palmetto	*Serenoa repens*, cabbage palm, dwarf palm, palmetto scrub	Prostate enlargement and bladder disorders, hair loss, prostate cancer
Soy	*Glycine max*, isoflavones, soy isoflavones	High cholesterol, cardiovascular disease prevention, menopausal symptoms, weight loss, arthritis, mental function, exercise performance
Spirulina	*Arthrospira* spp.	Allergies, diabetes, high cholesterol, fatigue, weight loss
St. John's wort	*Hypericum perforatum*	Depression, anxiety, obsessive-compulsive disorder, pain, menopausal symptoms, premenstrual syndrome
Valerian root	*Valeriana officinalis*	Anxiety, depression, insomnia, sedation, menopausal symptoms
Yohimbe	*Pausinystalia yohimbe*, yohimbine, yohimbe bark extract	Athletic performance, sexual dysfunction/libido enhancement, orthostatic hypotension

*Dosing for herbal products is not provided. Optimal dosing of natural products is often unclear; preparation of products varies and standardization may not be possible. Effects of different brands and dosage forms may not be comparable. Pharmacy technicians should consult the pharmacist for all natural products and dosing recommendations.
⁺Listed uses do not imply proven effectiveness for any indication. Herbal products are used for a wide range of conditions, but evidence supporting safety and effectiveness varies widely.

V. Chapter Summary

A. A drug's effectiveness and safety are affected by its appropriate use for the correct indication, monitoring for side effects, avoidance of contraindication, and proper dosage. Pharmacy technicians should be aware of the most frequent uses, warnings, and adverse effects with commonly used medications.

VI. Questions for Discussion

A. Why are some drugs used off label? What are some examples of off-label uses of common drugs?

B. Why do dosage regimens vary widely for some medications?

C. Discuss common herbal supplement questions that might arise in practice. What potential strategies can you use for answering questions about herbal products?

D. Discuss strategies for finding accurate dosing information to verify a prescription or nonprescription drug dosage.

VII. Sample Questions

1. Which of the following is classified primarily as a central nervous system medication?

   a. ACE inhibitor
   b. statin
   c. asthma medication
   d. antidepressant

2. Which of the following occurs when the body's immune system reacts to a drug?

   a. allergy
   b. contraindication
   c. indication
   d. warning

3. Which of the following medications is used to treat diabetes?

   a. insulin
   b. sitagliptin
   c. pioglitazone
   d. all of the above

4. Alprazolam is used primarily to treat which of the following?

   a. asthma
   b. anxiety
   c. cancer
   d. acne

5. Ceftriaxone is used primarily to treat which of the following?

   a. breast cancer
   b. high blood pressure
   c. bacterial infections
   d. allergies

6. Which of the following agents are gastrointestinal drugs used to treat gastroesophageal reflux disease (GERD)?

   a. pantoprazole
   b. duloxetine
   c. etanercept
   d. insulin

7. Which of the following herbal supplements is commonly used to treat skin conditions and promote wound healing?

   a. echinacea
   b. aloe vera
   c. elderberry
   d. garlic

8. Which of the following herbal supplements is commonly used to treat nausea/vomiting?

   a. cranberry
   b. alfalfa
   c. ginger
   d. olive leaf

The **Answer Key** appears in **Section VIII**.

Notes:

Section II

Pharmacy Law and Regulations

Kristin W. Weitzel

Section II details information related to laws and regulations that impact pharmacy practice, including:

- recordkeeping requirements of controlled substances and other medications
- laws and regulations that affect daily pharmacy practice
- rules governing pharmacy operations and pharmacy technician licensure
- dispensing requirements for drugs under special risk management and restricted distribution programs

Chapter 3

Law and Regulation in Pharmacy Practice

I. Key Terms and Concepts

A. Federal and state laws regulate the practice of pharmacy. If federal and state laws differ, pharmacy technicians should follow the stricter law.

B. The term *adulteration* refers to any drug consisting of altered, dirty, or unclean product; or a drug that is prepared, packaged, or stored under unsanitary conditions, or prepared in unsafe containers.

C. The term *misbranding* refers to package labeling that is false or misleading about the identity of what is in the container, or fails to carry required warnings or instructions on product labeling.

D. The *Controlled Substances Act (CSA)* classified drugs with the potential for abuse or dependence into schedules. Legal requirements for controlled substances are generally stricter than those for noncontrolled medications.

E. Certain drug products have specific recordkeeping requirements, including controlled substances, recalled medications, repackaged drugs, and investigational drug products.

F. Regulatory agencies enforce standards and supervise the regulation of the pharmacy profession. Key regulatory agencies impacting pharmacy practice include Drug Enforcement Administration (DEA), Food and Drug Administration (FDA), and The Joint Commission (TJC).

II. Laws Affecting Pharmacy Practice

A. Laws govern pharmacy practice on the federal and state level. If federal and state laws conflict, pharmacy technicians should follow the stricter rule. Each pharmacy technician should stay up to date on the state laws that govern pharmacy practice in his or her respective state.

B. *Federal Food, Drug, and Cosmetic Act of 1938* stated that new drugs must be approved by the FDA. This act also defined the terms adulteration and misbranding.

1. *Adulteration* – product that is altered, dirty, or unclean; prepared, packaged, or stored under unsanitary conditions; or prepared in unsafe containers.

2. *Misbranding* – package labeling that contains false or misleading information about the identity of the substance in the container, or fails to carry required warnings or instructions on product labeling.

C. *Durham-Humphrey Amendment of 1951* separated drugs into prescription and nonprescription categories.

D. *Poison Prevention Packaging Act of 1970* required most prescription and nonprescription drugs to be packaged in child-resistant containers.

E. *Occupational Safety and Health Act of 1970* established the Occupational Safety and Health Administration (OSHA), which ensures a safe and healthful work environment.

1. OSHA requires that a *Material Safety Data Sheet (MSDS)* be used to ensure safety with hazardous chemicals. As detailed in **Sections IV and VI**, the MSDS provides data on toxicity and storage, instructions on cleaning spills, and other safety information for handling hazardous products such as chemotherapy medications.

F. In 1970 the CSA established distinct procedures for handling controlled substances versus noncontrolled medications in the pharmacy.

1. The CSA established five schedules of controlled substances.

   a. Schedule I: Extremely high potential for abuse, no accepted medical use (e.g., heroin, cocaine).

   b. Schedule II: High abuse potential which may lead to severe psychological or physical dependence (e.g., methadone, oxycodone, morphine).

   c. Schedule III: Less abuse potential than Schedules 1 and 2, but may lead to psychological or physical dependence (e.g., hydrocodone combination products).

   d. Schedule IV: Low potential for abuse relative to Schedule 3 substances (e.g., alprazolam).

   e. Schedule V: Low potential for abuse relative to Schedule 4 substances (e.g., cough preparations containing minimal codeine).

G. *Omnibus Budget Reconciliation Act of 1990* required pharmacists to perform a drug therapy review and offer medication counseling to patients or their caregivers for all prescriptions filled.

H. *Health Insurance Portability and Accountability Act (HIPAA) of 1996* required that health care providers ensure patient confidentiality.

1. Pharmacy technicians should follow HIPAA laws to ensure that a patient's protected health information is not disclosed inappropriately.

I. *Combat Methamphetamine Epidemic Act of 2005* subjected pseudoephedrine and other agents used in the illegal manufacture of methamphetamine ("crystal meth") to restricted sales, storage, and recordkeeping requirements.

   1. Sales of pseudoephedrine were limited to 3.6 g/day or 9 g/30-day period.

J. *USP <797>* established procedures and quality assurance requirements for facilities involved in the preparation, storage, or dispensing of sterile products to help ensure product sterility and decrease contamination. *USP <795>* established procedures and quality assurance requirements for nonsterile compounding. **Section IV** contains more information on these standards and guidelines.

K. The *Resource Conservation and Recovery Act* provides guidance for disposal of hazardous and nonhazardous waste. Pharmacies must comply with these guidelines when disposing of pharmaceutical waste. Depending on the type of waste stream, additional federal or state regulations may apply. **Section VI** contains more information on these guidelines.

L. *State Pharmacy Practice Acts* provide additional rules and laws for pharmacy practice that differ in each state. Pharmacy technicians should familiarize themselves with laws affecting pharmacy practice within their state.

   1. A state's Pharmacy Practice Act governs how generic and brand product substitutions are made and how principles of therapeutic equivalence are applied under state law. **Chapter 1** contains more detailed information on therapeutic equivalence.

   For example, many states adopt a "positive formulary" approach, in which brand and generic products listed as therapeutically equivalent in the FDA's *Orange Book* can always be substituted for one another. Other states utilize a "negative formulary" approach, in which they identify a defined list of branded products that cannot be substituted with generics without prescriber approval.

III. Pharmacy Regulatory Agencies

A. Regulatory agencies are established to enforce standards set forth in pharmacy-related laws, ensure public safety, and supervise the regulation of the pharmacy profession.

B. *Centers for Medicare and Medicaid Services (CMS)* oversee Medicare and Medicaid.

C. The DEA enforces prescriber and pharmacy compliance with the Controlled Substances Act.

D. The FDA oversees drug purity, safety, and effectiveness; issues and monitors drug recalls if products are adulterated or misbranded; regulates patient package inserts; and reviews applications for new and investigational drugs.

E. Accrediting bodies set standards and grant accreditation to promote patient safety and quality of care. *The Joint Commission*, previously known as Joint Commission on Accreditation of Healthcare Organizations (JCAHO), sets standards and grants accreditation to health care organizations to promote patient safety and quality of care. The *Center for Pharmacy Practice Accreditation* develops and implements accreditation programs for community pharmacies.

F. *State Boards of Pharmacy (BOP)* regulate pharmacy practice within each state. The *National Association of Boards of Pharmacy (NABP)* is made up of all of the state BOPs.

IV. Pharmacy Recordkeeping Requirements

A. Records of all prescriptions must be kept on file either as hard copies or electronically, as required by state law.

Federal and state laws also require separate records to be maintained for some drug products, including controlled substances, recalled medications, repackaged products, and investigational drugs.

B. Controlled Substances

1. Ordering controlled substances: DEA Form 222 is used for ordering Schedule II controlled substances, with records maintained for two years.

2. Receiving and storing controlled substances: Documentation of controlled substances may also require the following information:

    a. Date the drug was received

    b. Drug name, strength, dosage form, and quantity received

    c. Initials of technician and supervising pharmacist

    d. Other information as required by pharmacy policies

3. Returning controlled substances: DEA Form 222 is also used when transferring Schedule II drugs to any other party registered to the DEA, such as returning Schedule II drugs to a reverse distributor for disposal or partial credit. Returning other scheduled drugs may require documenting the following information, as specified by pharmacy policies and procedures:

    a. Date the drug was removed from inventory

    b. Drug name, strength, dosage form, and quantity removed

    c. Lot number

    d. Purpose for removing the drug from inventory (e.g., manufacturer recall)

e. Initials of technician and supervising pharmacist

f. Other information as required by pharmacy policies

4. Destruction of outdated or damaged controlled substances: DEA Form 41 must be submitted, including documentation of witnesses present for the destruction.

5. Theft of controlled substances: DEA Form 106 must be completed upon theft of controlled substances, after the local DEA diversion office and police are notified.

C. Recalled medications (detailed in **Chapter 13**)

1. Documenting recalls and returns may require entering the following information into the inventory records:

a. Date the product was removed from inventory

b. Information to identify the product

(1) Pharmaceuticals
(a) Drug name, strength, dosage form, and quantity removed

(2) Equipment, devices, and supplies
(a) Product name, size, and any other pertinent information for identification

c. Product manufacturer

d. Lot number or identification number

e. Purpose for removing the drug from inventory (e.g., manufacturer recall)

f. Initials of technician and supervising pharmacist

g. Other information as required by pharmacy policies

D. Repackaged medications

1. Repackaged drug products must be labeled with the following information:

a. Generic drug name

b. Drug strength

c. Dosage form

d. Manufacturer's name and lot number

e. Expiration date after repackaging, according to federal law mandates

2. A repackaging log may also need to be maintained in the pharmacy.

E. Investigational Drugs

1. Recordkeeping procedures for investigational drug programs follow guidelines set by federal agencies and investigators.

2. The pharmacy will record the following information about every investigational drug:

   a. Date and time received.

   b. Packing slip details, including shipping information, shipping contents (e.g., drug, diluents), principal investigator, and the proper protocol.

   c. Proper storage requirements, determined by temperature and lighting (refrigerated, nonrefrigerated, light sensitive).

   d. Investigational drugs, labeled with drug name, strength, administration, expiration date, and the number assigned to the study. Investigational drugs should be kept in a permanent storage space, separate from other medications.

V. Operational Licensing Requirements of Pharmacies

A. A pharmacy must meet the following requirements to legally maintain operation. These requirements vary by state and type of pharmacy license:

1. Business license.

2. Pharmacy license. Some states require specialty pharmacy licenses (e.g., nuclear, long-term care).

3. Licensed pharmacist. Some states may require a designated pharmacist-in-charge.

4. Meets requirements for storage and documentation of prescription records and medication.

B. State BOPs conduct periodic inspections to ensure compliance with legal and regulatory requirements for space, facilities, prescription file storage, and medication reference materials. Additional requirements may also exist from accrediting or regulatory agencies, such as TJC or U.S. Pharmacopoeia (USP).

VI. Roles and Requirements of the Pharmacy Technician

A. The NABP defines pharmacy technicians as "personnel registered with the Board who may, under the supervision of the pharmacist, assist in the pharmacy and perform such functions as assisting in the dispensing process; processing medical coverage claims; stocking medications; cashiering, but excluding drug regimen review; clinical conflict resolution; prescriber contact concerning prescription drug order clarification or therapy modification; patient counseling; dispensing process validation; prescription transfer; and receipt of new prescription drug orders."

B. State BOPs regulate the requirements of pharmacy technician certification and practice on the state level. Technicians should be knowledgeable about practice and certification requirements in their state.

VII. Chapter Summary

A. Technicians should familiarize themselves with key pharmacy laws and regulatory agencies overseeing the practice of pharmacy. Failure to comply with laws and regulations could result in professional licensure action, monetary fines, or in rare cases, personal liability.

B. New drugs are approved by the FDA and manufactured, packaged, prescribed, and dispensed according to established pharmacy laws.

C. Regulation of medication manufacturing, packaging, storage, prescribing, and dispensing is overseen by the FDA, DEA, and CMS.

D. Technicians should learn specific recordkeeping requirements for controlled substances, recalled or repackaged products, and investigational drugs.

E. Standards, accreditation, and inspection for quality procedures and patient safety in pharmacies and health care organizations are coordinated primarily through state BOPs and accrediting agencies such as TJC.

VIII. Questions for Discussion

A. Discuss the difference between a pharmacy law and a regulatory agency.

B. What is the difference between adulteration and misbranding? Which regulatory agency issues drug recalls if a product is adulterated or misbranded?

C. Why are dispensing and documentation requirements stricter for controlled substances? List some examples of commonly dispensed controlled substances.

D. What are the functions of the FDA?

E. Discuss the reasons for additional recordkeeping requirements with some categories of drug products. How do these contribute to patient safety and prevent adverse consequences?

F. How does an accreditation or inspection process help support patient safety and quality patient care? Which regulatory agencies have this role in pharmacy practice?

IX. Sample Questions

1. Which of the following laws required the use of child-resistant packaging for drug products?

    a. Durham-Humphrey Act
    b. Controlled Substances Act
    c. Poison Prevention Act
    d. Pure Food and Drug Act

2. An injectable drug is found to be contaminated with dust and debris introduced in the manufacturing process. This is an example of which of the following?

    a. adulteration
    b. misbranding
    c. mislabeling
    d. packaging

3. Which of the following laws ensures that health care providers maintain confidentiality of a patient's protected health information?

    a. Controlled Substances Act
    b. Health Insurance Portability and Accountability Act
    c. Combat Methamphetamine Act
    d. Omnibus Budget Reconciliation Act of 1990

4. Which of the following must be completed when controlled substances are returned?

    a. DEA Form 222
    b. DEA Form 106
    c. DEA Form 41
    d. DEA Form 32

5. Heroin has no accepted medical use and an extremely high potential for abuse. It is classified as which of the following by the Controlled Substances Act?

    a. Schedule I
    b. Schedule II
    c. Schedule III
    d. Schedule IV

6. Which of the following regulatory agencies issues and monitors drug recalls?

    a. Centers for Medicare and Medicaid Services
    b. Bureau of Alcohol, Tobacco, Firearms, and Explosives
    c. Drug Enforcement Administration
    d. Food and Drug Administration

7. Which of the following agencies sets standards for quality and patient safety and accredits health care organizations?

    a. Food and Drug Administration
    b. Drug Enforcement Administration
    c. The Joint Commission
    d. State Boards of Pharmacy

8. Which of the following governs therapeutic equivalence and substitution between generic and brand products?

    a. Controlled Substances Act
    b. State Pharmacy Practice Act
    c. Drug Enforcement Administration
    d. The Joint Commission

9. Which of the following must be completed when controlled substances are destroyed?

    a. DEA Form 222
    b. DEA Form 106
    c. DEA Form 41
    d. DEA Form 32

The **Answer Key** appears in **Section VIII**.

Notes:

Chapter 4

Risk Management and Restricted Drug Programs

I. Key Terms and Concepts

A. Some drugs are approved by the Food and Drug Administration (FDA) but require special monitoring or educational communication to minimize risk and ensure appropriate use.

B. *Patient package inserts* were an early form of risk management strategy to inform patients of risks with oral contraceptives and estrogen-containing products.

C. *Restricted distribution drug programs* were put in place in the 1990s and early 2000s to allow for efficacy and safety monitoring for drugs that have limited use because of side effects and unintended consequences. Examples of these drugs include clozaril and isotretinoin products.

D. The FDA was granted legislative authority in 2007 to establish *Risk Evaluation and Mitigation Strategies (REMS)* to help manage serious risks associated with drug products, such as transmucosal immediate-release fentanyl products, and topical testosterone agents.

E. The pharmacy technician assists the pharmacist in dispensing and recording the distribution of agents subject to special dispensing requirements.

II. Risk Management

A. In the 1970s, the FDA began requiring *patient package inserts* to be dispensed with oral contraceptives and estrogen-containing drug products. These were among the FDA's first formal efforts to communicate specific drug risks to patients through added labeling.

B. During the 1990s, "restricted distribution" or "restricted access" programs limited availability of selected drug products to help ensure appropriate use and minimize risks. These products included:

1. Clozapine (Clozaril®)

    a. To help detect and prevent life-threatening agranulocytosis and other cardiovascular and respiratory effects, registration and monitoring with the IVAX Pharmaceuticals Clozapine Patient Registry or the Clozaril National Registry is required prior to dispensing a 7- to 14-day supply of clozapine.

b. A current and acceptable white blood cell count is required, with routine monitoring.

2. Other drugs formerly classified as "restricted distribution" have been transitioned into REMS programs, including thalidomide (Thalomid®), isotretinoin products (Accutane®, Amnesteem®, Claravis®, Sotret®), and dofetilide (Tikosyn®).

C. *The Food and Drug Administration Amendments Act of 2007* granted the FDA authority to require REMS programs from manufacturers.

1. REMS programs are instituted when the FDA deems that using specific strategies to increase patient awareness and education about safety and appropriate use can minimize a drug's risk.

2. Required REMS components may include a medication guide, elements to ensure safe use, a communication plan, and/or an implementation system.

III. Medication Guides

A. The FDA can require a *medication guide* as part of a REMS program if one or more of the following circumstances exist:

1. Patient labeling could help prevent serious adverse effects related to the drug;

2. The drug poses serious risks relative to benefits, which could affect patients' decision to use, or continue to use, the product; or

3. Patient adherence to directions for the drug's use is crucial to the drug's effectiveness and important to health.

B. If a medication guide is required as part of a REMS program, the guide must be dispensed to the patient or the patient's representative upon request, or each time that a drug is dispensed in an outpatient setting and will be used without the supervision of a health care professional.

A medication guide may also be required in other circumstances, such as after a significant change to the medication guide, or if the REMS requires medication guide review with the patient to ensure safe use.

C. Some examples of drugs requiring a medication guide as the only component of a REMS program are listed below:

1. Topical testosterone products (Androgel, Axiron, Testim, Fortesta)
2. Varenicline (Chantix)
3. Metoclopramide oral solution
4. Tapentadol tablets
5. Bupropion hydrochloride sustained-release (Zyban)

D. A medication guide can also be required as part of a larger program that incorporates other REMS elements, such as individual REMS requirements or shared system REMS requirements.

IV. Individual REMS Requirements

A. An individual REMS program exists when the REMS requirements apply only to a single drug in a given category or class. Drug products with significant individual REMS requirements include:

1. Epogen/Procrit (epoetin alfa) injection:

    a. REMS requirements include a medication guide, communication plan, elements to ensure safe use, and an implementation system to inform patients of cardiac and cancer-related risks.

    b. For oncology patients, a pharmacist or other representative must be trained and certified in the ESA (Erythropoiesis Stimulating Agent) APPRISE (Assisting Providers and cancer Patients with Risk Information for the Safe use of ESAs) Oncology program and participate in compliance monitoring.

    c. Patients and prescribing physicians sign an ESA Oncology Patient and Healthcare Professional Acknowledgement Form to document that the risks and benefits of the drug product have been discussed.

2. Thalidomide (Thalomid®):

    a. REMS requirements include a medication guide, elements to ensure safe use, and an implementation system to ensure that women of childbearing age do not use or handle thalidomide because of teratogenicity risk.

    b. Prescribers, patients, and pharmacists who prescribe, receive, and dispense thalidomide must be registered in the S.T.E.P.S.® (System for Thalidomide Education and Prescribing Safety) restricted distribution program.

    c. Quantity dispensed is limited to 28 days with an original prescription (no telephone prescriptions or automatic refills). Pregnancy testing and birth control are required.

    d. Pharmacists must receive authorization via an interactive voice response system to verify that patient and physician requirements are met in order to dispense the prescription.

3. Alosetron (Lotronex™)

    a. Alosetron is subject to use under the Prescribing Program for Lotronex to minimize risk of life-threatening ischemic colitis and complications of constipation, including death.

    b. REMS requirements include a medication guide, enrollment and self-certification of physicians, and completion of a patient-physician agreement form.

    c. Only written prescriptions are permitted and a prescribing program sticker is required on all written prescriptions.

V. Shared System REMS Requirements

A. Drug products with shared system REMS have the same REMS requirements for multiple drugs in a category or class. Drug products with significant shared system REMS requirements include:

1. Isotretinoin products (Accutane®, Amnesteem®, Claravis®, Sotret®)

    a. REMS requirements include a medication guide, elements to ensure safe use, and an implementation system to prevent teratogenic effects of fetal exposure to isotretinoin.

    b. Prescribers, pharmacies, and patients are required to register with the iPLEDGE program to prescribe, dispense, and receive isotretinoin by prescription. A "responsible site pharmacist" must be designated to dispense only to approved patients and document the patient authorization number.

    c. Patient education, ongoing pregnancy testing, and birth control use are required. Only a 30-day supply may be dispensed.

    d. The manufacturer is required to monitor drug distribution, ensure patient, physician, and pharmacy compliance with iPLEDGE program requirements to maintain active program status, and maintain an isotretinoin pregnancy database.

2. Extended-release and long-acting opioid analgesics

    a. REMS requirements include a medication guide and training for health care providers who prescribe extended-release and long-acting opioid analgesics to decrease risk of adverse effects from inappropriate prescribing, misuse, and abuse of these drug products.

3. Transmucosal immediate-release fentanyl products (Abstral, Actiq, Fentora, Lazanda, Onsolis, Subsys):

    a. REMS requirements include a medication guide, elements to ensure safe use, and an implementation system to mitigate risks of misuse, abuse, overdose, and serious complications.

    b. Prescribers must become certified to prescribe transmucosal immediate-release fentanyl products by reviewing education materials and completing the prescriber enrollment form. Patients and prescribers must complete an agreement form, which must be renewed every 2 years.

    c. Pharmacies must be certified to dispense these drug products. Education programs and enrollment forms differ for outpatient, closed-system, and inpatient pharmacies.

VI. Chapter Summary

A. Pharmacy technicians must remember that some drugs provide effective therapy but are associated with serious risks. However, when certain conditions are met, these drugs may provide the most effective therapy for particular patients.

B. Compliance with REMS programs is a regulatory requirement. A REMS drug dispensed outside of program compliance may be considered misbranded or place the patient at an unacceptable level of risk.

C. Pharmacy technicians play an important role in supporting the pharmacist in ensuring compliance with REMS programs in pharmacy practice.

VII. Questions for Discussion

A. With all the potential adverse effects, why are restricted drugs still on the market?

B. When handling thalidomide tablets, what is the primary concern facing the technician, pharmacist, or nurse?

C. How can medication guides help decrease risks with drug products?

D. Why were the REMS programs created?

E. What is the pharmacy technician's role in REMS programs?

F. Where can pharmacy technicians find out if their pharmacy participates in a specific REMS program?

VIII. Sample Questions

1. Which of the following classes of medications must be dispensed with a patient package insert?

   a. oral contraceptives
   b. antihypertensives
   c. cholesterol-lowering medications
   d. corticosteroids

2. Patients getting a clozapine prescription must do which of the following?

   a. document a negative pregnancy test
   b. enroll in the iPLEDGE program
   c. comply with required white blood cell count monitoring
   d. pass a written test on clozapine risks

3. A medication guide is required for which of the following drugs?

    a. lisinopril
    b. simvastatin
    c. diphenhydramine
    d. varenicline

4. A REMS program may include which of the following elements?

    a. communication plan
    b. elements to ensure safe use
    c. medication guide
    d. all of the above

5. Participation in the S.T.E.P.S.® risk management program allows patients to receive which of the following drugs?

    a. fentanyl
    b. thalidomide
    c. isotretinoin
    d. epoetin alfa

6. Participation in the ESA APPRISE risk management program allows pharmacies to dispense which of the following drug products?

    a. clozaril
    b. varenicline
    c. epoetin alfa
    d. thalidomide

7. Pharmacies must be certified to dispense which of the following drug products?

    a. transmucosal immediate-release fentanyl
    b. hydrocodone
    c. varenicline
    d. metoclopramide

The **Answer Key** appears in **Section VIII**.

Notes:

Section 

Medication Order Entry and Fill Process

Kristin W. Weitzel

Section III explains activities related to prescription dispensing and medication distribution, including:

- receiving and processing prescriptions and medication orders
- obtaining and entering information in the patient profile
- managing information in pharmacy databases and computer systems
- obtaining prescription reimbursement from third parties

Chapter 5

Pharmacy Computer and Patient Information Systems

I. Key Terms and Concepts

A. A *patient profile* is a record containing information about a specific patient including demographic information, medical history, medication use chronology, allergies, and chronic illnesses.

B. The *diagnosis* is the identified disease or health condition determined by the prescriber through assessment of the patient's signs and symptoms.

C. The *desired therapeutic outcome* is the desired result of drug therapy. The outcome may be an end result (e.g., complete cure of the disease), a disease-related goal (e.g., lowering and maintaining blood pressure to an acceptable level), or a general therapy goal (e.g., an appropriate level of sedation prior to surgery).

D. *Electronic health or medical records* are used by some pharmacies as part of a larger electronic health system. A patient's medication profile may be accessible in concert with other medical information (labs, diagnoses, etc.) in different areas of a health system.

E. *Medication reconciliation* is the process of reviewing a patient's complete medication list for accuracy each time the patient undergoes a transition of care.

II. Computer-Based Pharmacy Systems

A. Pharmacy computer systems perform various information management and database functions, including:

1. Processing prescription and medication orders
2. Controlling inventory
3. Tracking controlled substances
4. Updating drug prices

5. Assisting with administrative functions

    a. Workload and productivity tracking

    b. Drug utilization review

    c. Third-party authorization, billing, and reconciliation

6. Maintaining and gathering patient information

    a. Electronic health or medical records

    b. Patient indicators or outcomes (e.g., adherence, achievement of therapeutic goals)

    c. Specific characteristics for risk management or other purposes (e.g., incidence of drug allergies or side effects with a given medication)

B. Pharmacy computer systems also provide database-managed information, such as:

1. Drug usage and trends, drug databases, and pharmacy overrides

2. Inventory levels

3. Third-party audits

4. Formulary or prescribing trends

5. Drug diversion reports

C. All pharmacy computer and information systems must comply with professional standards related to data integrity, security, and confidentiality. These include, but are not limited to, appropriate policies and procedures for:

1. Restricting and reporting user access to information.

2. Establishing procedures for backing up and archiving patient and pharmacy data for retrieval and security.

3. Compliance with the Health Insurance Portability and Accountability Act measures for protected health information.

III. Obtaining Patient Information to Be Entered in the Patient Profile System

A. Obtaining patient information

1. At the pharmacist's direction, technicians may need to obtain patient information from the patient/patient's representative, prescriber, or other health professional. This information will be used to create or update the patient profile.

   To obtain accurate information, technicians should possess good communication skills and learn appropriate patient interviewing techniques.

B. Patient profiles may be manual or computerized records. The patient profile may include:

1. Patient information

   a. Ambulatory/outpatient setting
      (1) Patient's name, birth date, address, telephone number, pertinent insurance reimbursement information

   b. Institutional/inpatient setting

      (1) Patient's name, birth date, address, height, weight, identification number, room number, primary physician

2. Diagnosis

3. Desired therapeutic outcome

4. Medication use

   a. The patient's medication history and current medication use (including nonprescription drugs) are critical to assessing the appropriateness of therapy. This information can help detect potential drug interactions, possible allergies, duplicate therapy, and other potential problems. The outpatient profile should include a chronology of medication refills.

5. Allergies

   a. The patient's history of allergies can help predict potential allergies to similar drugs.

6. Adverse reactions

   a. The patient's history of adverse reactions can help predict potential adverse reactions to similar drugs.

7. Medical history

   a. This includes a chronology of past and current medical conditions.

8. Psychosocial history

   a. This information can indicate potential influences on patient compliance, drug misuse, drug abuse, and other factors. In some cases, the pharmacist may need to give the patient additional instructions or counseling.

9. Patient characteristics/special considerations

   a. Some characteristics may require special attention when processing the patient's prescriptions. Addressing these factors will help prevent potential problems (e.g., poor adherence, drug misuse). Patients with limitations may require special labeling, packaging, and auxiliary materials (e.g., instructions written in large print or in another language), or counseling by the pharmacist. Examples include:

      (1) Physical characteristics

         (a) Visual impairment
         (b) Hearing impairment
         (c) Other physical disabilities

      (2) Sociological characteristics

         (a) Foreign language
         (b) Cultural or religious beliefs

10. Socioeconomic history

11. Reimbursement mechanisms and third-party payer (prescription insurance) information

   a. This function includes questioning the patient/patient's representative about the payment method, and assessing the eligibility of the patient and the prescribed product for reimbursement from the patient's third-party payer.

C. Collecting data to monitor patient outcomes

1. At the pharmacist's direction, technicians may collect data that will help the pharmacist monitor patient outcomes. Tests may include:

   a. Blood pressure measurements in persons with preexisting or suspected hypertension.

   b. Glucose (blood sugar) levels in patients with diabetes, those suspected of having diabetes, or pregnant women who have had problems with elevated glucose levels.

c. Cholesterol levels in patients with preexisting or suspected heart disease or coronary artery disease.

IV. Entering Patient Information into the Patient Profile System

A. New patients

1. Patient profiles are generated for every patient receiving medication from the pharmacy department. Working with the pharmacist, technicians may need to create a profile for each new patient who receives a prescription from the pharmacy.

B. Patients with existing profiles

1. Updating the medical record/patient profile

a. Because the patient's health status and/or response to medications may change, patient profiles must be updated each time any information changes. The patient/patient's representative may not automatically volunteer this information. Therefore, at the pharmacist's direction, technicians may interview patients about possible changes in their health condition or medication use. Any item listed in the patient profile may require updating.

Changes in patient information other than demographics (e.g., address) should be brought to the pharmacist's attention immediately for patient counseling.

The most common changes include:

(1) Patient information. Ask the patient/patient's representative whether this information is current and correct.

(2) Diagnosis or desired therapeutic outcome. Has anything changed regarding the patient's disease or condition? Are there any new problems?

(3) Medication use. Is the patient still using the medications listed in the patient profile? Have any new prescription or nonprescription medications been added to the regimen?

(4) Allergies. Has the patient experienced allergic symptoms that may be related to current drug therapy?

(5) Adverse reactions. Has the patient experienced adverse reactions that may be related to current drug therapy?

(6) Reimbursement mechanisms and third-party payer information. Is this information current and correct?

(7) Medication duplication. When updating the patient profile, be aware of possible duplicate medications. If discovered, notify the pharmacist immediately.

(8) Drug interactions. Remain aware of the potential for drug interactions. Prescription drugs may interact with other prescription drugs, nonprescription drugs, food, and some laboratory tests.

C. Electronic health or medical records

1. Electronic health records are defined as pharmacy-related computer applications for documenting the dispensing of prescriptions or medication orders (e.g., maintaining the electronic medical record, patient adherence, risk factors, alcohol and drug use, drug allergies, side effects).

2. Electronic health records provide a shared electronic system for storing a patient's medical and drug therapy information, rather than the pharmacy maintaining a separate patient drug profile. Electronic records can facilitate information sharing among different practitioners and decrease health-related and medication errors.

3. Pharmacy patient profiles in larger health systems and hospitals may be integrated into a larger electronic health records system.

4. Technicians entering and retrieving patient and pharmacy data to and from electronic health or medical records systems should know how data are processed within the system as a whole to optimize safety and avoid errors (for example, if a patient profile is changed by a nurse on the floor instead of in the pharmacy).

D. Medication reconciliation

1. Patients often have changes made to their medication regimen when they transition from one level of care to another, such as when a patient is admitted to or discharged from the hospital. If these drug therapy changes are not transmitted correctly, patients are at risk for adverse events because of duplicate therapy, inappropriately discontinued medications, continuation of a drug that should be stopped, or related problems.

2. *Medication reconciliation* is the process of reviewing a patient's complete medication list to ensure its accuracy each time a transition of care is made. Technicians may be involved in the medication reconciliation process to ensure that a patient's medication list is current and accurate at each transition of care and help to improve patient safety.

3. When reconciling a patient's medication list, technicians should question patients about prescription and nonprescription medications, as well as alternative medications and dietary supplements.

V. Chapter Summary

A. Pharmacy computer systems are essential to patient and pharmacy information management.

B. Developing and maintaining patient profile systems are primary responsibilities of technicians in both inpatient and outpatient settings.

C. Technicians must understand patient profile information and identify any important changes that require special attention by the pharmacist.

D. Pharmacy technicians may assist the pharmacist in obtaining patient information by conducting interviews with patients or their representatives, and with health care professionals. To do this effectively, technicians must possess good communication skills and be proficient in various interviewing techniques. Obtaining information about a patient's diagnosis, desired therapeutic outcome, medication use, allergies, and other pertinent data remains essential to providing complete pharmaceutical care.

E. Medication reconciliation is crucial to ensuring the accuracy and completeness of a patient's medication record.

VI. Questions for Discussion

A. Accepting new prescriptions/medication orders may require the technician to interview the patient/patient's representative about certain types of information.

1. What types of questions should you ask a new patient?
2. What questions should you ask a patient who has an existing patient profile?

B. Describe examples of how a pharmacy computer database system can help with maintaining patient and drug information in the pharmacy.

C. How do pharmacy-related computer applications assist in documentation management?

D. Describe examples of medication and/or medication class duplication.

E. Discuss the importance of good communication skills in patient interviewing. What communication skills are most important?

VII. Sample Questions

1. Pharmacy computer database systems can assist with maintenance of which of the following?

    a. inventory control
    b. controlled substances documentation
    c. drug pricing
    d. all of the above

2. Which of the following describes a strategy to comply with professional standards related to data integrity, security, and confidentiality?

    a. following established procedures for backing up and archiving patient data
    b. maintaining current address information in a patient profile
    c. failing to document a patient allergy change
    d. using a Windows-based computer system

3. Which of the following can help predict a patient's potential drug allergies?

    a. date of birth
    b. previous allergic reactions
    c. previous adverse drug reactions
    d. psychosocial history

4. Which of the following is an example of a patient limitation that may necessitate special prescription packaging or labeling?

    a. previous adverse drug reactions
    b. previous allergic reactions
    c. visual impairment
    d. history of drug abuse

5. How often should a patient's profile be updated?

    a. each time that a patient's information (address, medication list, etc.) changes
    b. never
    c. every year
    d. every 10 years

6. Which of the following is an example of a paperless patient profile system used to improve safety and quality of care in some health care systems?

    a. synergy systems
    b. electronic health records
    c. medication reconciliation
    d. desired therapeutic outcomes

7. The process of reviewing a patient's medication list to ensure accuracy at transitions of care is referred to as:

   a. electronic health records
   b. patient profiling
   c. desired therapeutic outcomes
   d. medication reconciliation

The **Answer Key** appears in **Section VIII**.

Notes:

Chapter 6

Receiving Prescriptions and Medication Orders

I. Key Terms and Concepts

A. A *prescription* is an order for the preparation and administration of a drug or nondrug remedy issued by a licensed medical practitioner who is authorized by state law to prescribe.

Prescriptions can be presented to the pharmacy in written form or via telephone, fax, or computer, depending on individual state laws. Prescribers can include physicians, dentists, veterinarians, nurse practitioners, and physician assistants. Prescriptions are usually filled in an outpatient pharmacy for patient use on an ambulatory basis.

B. A *medication order,* like a prescription, is a written order for the preparation and administration of medication, issued by a licensed medical practitioner who is authorized to prescribe. Medication orders are intended for patients in an inpatient (e.g., institutional, hospital) setting.

II. Understanding Prescriptions and Medication Orders

A. Prescriptions should contain the following information:

1. Patient information

    a. The patient's name, age, address, and telephone number.

2. Date

    a. The date the prescriber wrote the prescription order.

3. Name of the product

    a. The drug name can be written as either the generic or trade name.

4. Strength of the product

    a. The strength should always be included to avoid misinterpretation. Exceptions include if only one strength is commercially available, or if otherwise inappropriate (e.g., devices).

Strength may also be excluded in products that consist of a combination of two or more drugs for which only one drug:drug concentration ratio is commercially available.

5. Dosage form

   a. If only one form is commercially available, the dosage form may not be included. **Chapter 1** contains more information on product strength, dose, and dosage form, as well as a list of common dosage forms.

6. Quantity of medication to be dispensed

   a. The quantity represents the number of units or dosage forms (e.g., tablets, ounces, grams) to be dispensed. This amount may not be included in the prescription if the dispensing quantity can be calculated from the physician's directions and duration of therapy (e.g., 3-month supply). Quantity may also be written as q.s. *(a sufficient quantity)* or q.s. ad *(a sufficient quantity to make).*

7. Directions for preparation

   a. Instructions to the pharmacist for compounding or preparing a product may be included.

8. Directions for labeling

   a. Prescriber's instructions to the pharmacist on what information should be included on the prescription label.

9. Directions for the patient on the prescription label

   a. Instructions for the patient on how to use the medication properly. **Tables 6-1 and 6-2** list terminology and abbreviations frequently used for prescription directions.

      (1) Route of administration. **Chapter 1** contains information on drug administration routes.

      (2) Dosage and dosage schedule. The quantity of medication to be taken by the patient and the schedule (frequency and/or time) of administration.

10. Refill information

    a. The prescriber's instructions for the number of refills that may be dispensed from the prescription order. If no information is provided, no refills are authorized. A prescriber may also write "no refills" or "NR" on the prescription order.

11. Prescriber information

    a. Prescriber's name, address, and telephone number.

b. Prescriber's Drug Enforcement Administration (DEA) number. **Chapter 7** outlines the formula for validating DEA numbers.

(1) The DEA number is a unique number assigned to practitioners, hospitals, and pharmacies to keep track of controlled drug distribution and prescriptions.

c. Prescriber's signature (unless the prescription is received by telephone).

TABLE 6-1. **Common Abbreviations Used in Prescriptions and Medical Orders**

Abbreviation	Meaning	Abbreviation	Meaning
a	before	NR	no refill
a.a. or aa	of each	o.d.	right eye
a.c.	before meals	o.l. or o.s.	left eye
a.d.	right ear	o.u.	both eyes
a.m.	morning	oz.	ounce
ante	before	p	after
aq.	aqueous (water)	p.c.	after meals
a.s.	left ear	p.m.	afternoon; evening
a.u.	each ear	p.o.	by mouth
b.i.d.	twice a day	p.r.	per rectum
c. or c	with	p.r.n.	as needed
cc.	cubic centimeter (milliliter)	pt.	pint
D.A.W.	dispense as written	q.	every
D.C., dc, or disc.	discontinue	q.d.	every day
disp.	dispense	q.h.	every hour
dx	diagnosis	q.h.s.	every bedtime
g or gm or Gm	gram	q.i.d.	four times a day
gal.	gallon	q.o.d.	every other day
gr.	grain	q.s.	a sufficient quantity
gtt.	drop	q.s. ad	a sufficient quantity to make
h.s.	at bedtime	qt.	quart
IM	intramuscular	s. or $\bar{s}$	without
inj.	injection	Sig.	write on label
IV	intravenous	SL, sl	sublingual
IVP	intravenous push	stat	immediately
IVPB	intravenous piggyback	s.c. or s.q.	subcutaneously
L or l	liter	sol.	solution
lb.	pound	syr.	syrup
mcg or µg	microgram	tbsp. or T	tablespoonful
mEq	milliequivalent	t.i.d.	three times a day
mg	milligram	tr. or tinct.	tincture
ml or mL	milliliter	tsp. or t.	teaspoonful
non rep.	do not repeat	u.d.	as directed
NPO	nothing by mouth	ung.	ointment

TABLE 6-2. Common Abbreviations Related to Drug Products or Diseases

Cl	chloride	Mg	magnesium
D5NS	5% dextrose in 0.9% sodium chloride	Na	sodium
D5RL	5% dextrose in Ringer's lactate	NaCl	sodium chloride
D5W	5% dextrose in water	NS	normal saline (0.9% sodium chloride)
GI	gastrointestinal	NTG	nitroglycerin
H2O	water	RL	Ringer's lactate
K, K+	potassium	SSKI	saturated solution of potassium iodide
KCl	potassium chloride	TPN	total parenteral nutrition
LR	lactated Ringer's		

B. Medication orders

1. Patient information

   a. While every medication order may not include in-depth patient information (diagnosis, concurrent therapies, etc.), the patient profile should contain this information as transcribed from previous orders. Medication orders typically include the following information:

      (1) Patient's name, birth date, room number, identification number
      (2) Indication for use of the medication (why the drug is being ordered)
      (3) Allergies or other information necessary to process the medication order

2. Date the medication order was written

3. Time of day that the medication order was written

   a. Time is an important factor in the institutional setting where patients are cared for on a 24-hour basis.

4. Name of the product

   a. Generic and/or trade name of the product

5. Strength of the product

   a. The strength should always be included to avoid misinterpretation. Exceptions include if only one strength is commercially available, or if otherwise inappropriate (e.g., devices).

      Strength may also be excluded in products that consist of a combination of two or more drugs for which only one drug:drug concentration ratio is commercially available.

6. Dosage form

   a. The dosage form may not be included if only one form is commercially available. **Chapter 1** contains more information on product strength, dose, and dosage form, as well as a list of common dosage forms.

7. Prescriber information

   a. Name and signature of the prescriber. The prescriber is usually the patient's primary physician but may be another attending physician or resident. The signature of the prescriber is not required when the order is received verbally, either by telephone or through another authorized health care professional. In these cases, the name or initial of the recipient (e.g., attending registered nurse or pharmacist) must be included on the medication order.

8. Directions for preparation

   a. Instructions to the pharmacist for compounding or preparing a product may be included.

9. Directions for administration

   a. Instructions for the nurse or other health care provider on how to administer the medication properly.

      (1) Route of administration. **Chapter 1** contains information on drug administration routes.

      (2) Dosage and dosage schedule. The quantity of medication to be taken and the schedule (frequency and/or time) of administration.

   b. Duration of therapy. Instructions describing how long the patient should receive the medication.

   c. Other instructions for administration. Detailed information on administration and scheduling of the drug, such as start date for medication use, tapering dosages, administration times related to laboratory tests, etc.

III. Receiving New Prescriptions and Medication Orders

A. Accepting new prescriptions/medication orders from the patient/patient's representative, prescriber, or other health care professionals requires the technician to understand the information required on prescriptions and medication orders.

   1. Written orders

a. Ambulatory/outpatient setting

(1) Prescriptions may be presented to the pharmacy in various ways. In the outpatient setting, the patient or patient's representative typically brings new prescriptions to the pharmacy. Depending on state laws, the prescriber may also send written prescription orders via fax.

b. Institutional/inpatient setting

(1) In the institutional setting, a written medication order may be presented to the pharmacy department by a physician, nurse, other health care professional, or messenger; transmitted electronically through an in-house computer system; or sent to the pharmacy via a pneumatic tube system.

2. Electronic prescriptions/medication orders

a. Fax and computer-generated prescriptions/medication orders

(1) Fax and computer-generated orders are electronic versions of written orders and should be received and processed in the same manner.

3. Telephone orders

a. Verbal orders for medications (whether received by telephone or in person) may be accepted only by a licensed pharmacist or, in some states, by a supervised pharmacy intern. In the institutional setting, a registered nurse may also receive and transcribe telephone orders from the prescriber.

IV. Receiving Prescription Refill and Transfer Requests

A. Accepting refill requests from the patient/patient's representative or prescriber

1. Receiving refill requests requires the technician to understand what information is required to process refills and how to obtain appropriate authorization for refills if necessary.

B. Accepting refill requests electronically

1. Telephone orders

a. The following information should be obtained when receiving oral requests for refills from patients, patients' representatives, or prescribers:

(1) Patient's name and telephone number

(2) Prescription number

(3) Drug name, strength, and quantity

(4) Prescriber information

(5) Reimbursement mechanisms/third-party payer information

2. Fax and computer-generated refill requests

   a. The information listed above also should be included in fax requests for refills. Contact the prescriber if more information is needed.

C. Contacting prescribers for clarification/authorization of prescription or medication order refills

1. At the supervising pharmacist's direction, technicians may call prescribers to obtain authorization for prescription refills or to renew expired medication orders. The following information should be provided to the prescriber or the prescriber's representative:

   a. Pharmacy's name and telephone number

   b. Patient's name

   c. Drug name, strength, and quantity

   d. Date of last refill

   e. Prescription directions

   f. Information that needs to be clarified, confirmed, or authorized

D. Transferring and accepting transfers of prescriptions or medication orders

1. At the supervising pharmacist's direction and as allowed by state law, technicians may transfer prescriptions to another pharmacy or receive prescriptions transferred by another pharmacy.

   The following information should be provided to the pharmacy receiving the transfer, and requested by the technician or pharmacist accepting a transferred prescription:

   a. Pharmacy's name and telephone number

   b. Patient's name and telephone number

   c. Drug name, strength, quantity, and instructions for use

   d. Date of original prescription

   e. Date of last refill

f. Physician's name and telephone number

g. Name of technician and/or pharmacist sending and receiving the transferred prescription

h. Original prescription number

V. Assessing Prescriptions and Medication Orders

A. Assessing the prescription or medication order for accuracy and completeness requires the technician to understand the information being presented and to ask appropriate questions when necessary.

Evaluating the prescription or medication order should include checking the accuracy and completeness of the following:

1. Patient information. Using the criteria described above, ascertain that appropriate patient information is included on the prescription/medication order.

    a. Prescriptions

        (1) Patient's name, age, address, known allergies

    b. Medication orders

        (1) Patient's name, birth date, room number, identification number, allergies, indications, and any other pertinent information necessary for processing the medication order.

        Other relevant patient information (e.g., diagnosis) may be verified by checking the patient profile.

2. Drug and product availability

    a. Verify that the product or drug name, strength, and dosage form are written in a manner consistent with commercially available products. This requires knowledge of available products, prescription medications, dosage forms, strengths, etc.

3. Authenticity

    a. Assess whether the prescription/medication order appears to be legitimate (e.g., prescriber's signature is authentic).

4. Legality

    a. Assess whether the prescription/medication order is legal. This includes verifying that the order complies with federal and state laws, etc.

5. Reimbursement eligibility (**Chapter 8** contains more information on this topic)

    a. Determine whether the patient is covered by the appropriate insurance or third-party payer, and that the drug (and the quantity of drug prescribed) is eligible for reimbursement according to the payer's policies. Confirm that the pharmacy accepts the patient's insurance carrier.

    b. Assist the patient or the patient's representative in choosing the best payment assistance plan if multiple plans are available.

VI. Chapter Summary

A. As front-line health care practitioners, pharmacy technicians must understand all aspects of receiving prescriptions and medication orders.

B. Technicians should be familiar with information required on prescriptions and medication orders.

They must also know how to accept new orders, refill requests and transfers from health care professionals, and be able to assess orders for clarity, completeness, accuracy, authenticity, and legality.

VII. Questions for Discussion

A. Discuss various differences between prescription orders and medication orders (information requirements, intent, quantity to be dispensed, etc.).

B. What action should you take when a patient requests a refill of a prescription that does not have refills authorized?

C. What factors should you consider when evaluating the authenticity of a prescription/medication order?

D. What factors should you consider when evaluating the accuracy and completeness of a prescription/medication order?

E. Why is the time of day when a medication order is written important in the institutional setting? Discuss examples of problems that could occur when time is not included on the order.

F. What action should you take when the pharmacy receives a prescription faxed from a patient or a patient's representative?

VIII. Sample Questions

1. Which of the following is usually filled in an outpatient pharmacy for patient use on an ambulatory basis?

    a. medication order
    b. abbreviation
    c. prescription
    d. dosage

2. Medication orders are intended for patients in which of the following settings?

    a. inpatient
    b. outpatient
    c. ambulatory
    d. healthy

3. A prescription should contain:

    a. date the prescription was written
    b. name of the drug product
    c. quantity of medication to be dispensed
    d. all of the above

4. Which of the following pairs correctly matches the abbreviation with its meaning?

    a. a.c. : after meals
    b. p.r. : per rectum
    c. IV : intramuscular
    d. o.d. : left eye

5. Which of the following is TRUE regarding verbal or telephone prescription orders?

    a. Verbal orders can be accepted by a pharmacy technician
    b. Verbal orders are not valid unless followed up by a hard copy prescription
    c. Verbal orders can be given only by the prescribing physician
    d. Verbal orders may be accepted by a supervised pharmacy intern in some states

6. When receiving oral requests for refills, pharmacy technicians should ask for which of the following?

    a. Drug name, strength, and quantity
    b. Drug NDC number
    c. List of patient's other medications
    d. Names of patient's family members

7. A prescription that is sent to, or received from, another pharmacy to be dispensed is called a/an:

   a. refill
   b. order
   c. transfer
   d. electronic request

8. Which of the following pairs correctly matches the abbreviation with its meaning?

   a. Cl : Chloride
   b. K+ : Kayexalate
   c. NTG : Sodium
   d. LR : left and right eye

9. Which of the following is an order for the preparation and administration of a drug issued by a licensed medical practitioner who is authorized by state law to prescribe?

   a. facsimile
   b. sig
   c. transfer
   d. prescription

10. Which of the following information should be obtained when receiving a prescription transfer?

   a. transferring pharmacy's name and telephone number
   b. drug name, strength, quantity, and instructions for use
   c. date of original prescription
   d. all of the above

The **Answer Key** appears in **Section VIII**.

Notes:

Chapter 7

Processing Prescriptions and Medication Orders

I. Key Terms and Concepts

A. *Order entry* is the process of entering new prescription or medication information into an existing patient profile or creating a new patient profile.

B. *Drug utilization review* (DUR) *or drug utilization evaluation* (DUE) *alerts* are automated pharmacy computer system warnings used to alert pharmacists and technicians to potential medication errors or problems.

C. A *formulary* is a list of preferred or acceptable medications set by an individual or group of third-party payers or institutions.

D. *Unit-dose* packaging is used to package individual doses of a medication (e.g., blister packing).

II. Order Entry

A. Order entry

1. *Data* or *order entry* is the process of entering new prescription/medication information into an existing patient profile or creating a new patient profile. Order entry is usually the first step in processing prescriptions/medication orders. Pay strict attention to detail when performing this function because order-entry errors can directly affect patient safety.

   Order entry may also provide input into other systems. For example, entering the prescription/medication order into a computerized patient profile may simultaneously generate a prescription label, update the drug inventory record, create an entry into an electronic inventory ordering system, and update or change information in other databases. When entering new prescription/medication information, follow these steps:

   a. Verify the patient's name and/or identification number. If the patient already has an existing profile, confirm that the patient information on the new order matches the patient information on the profile. If you do not find an existing patient profile, you will need to create a new profile. **Chapter 5** contains more information on creating patient profiles.

b. Compare the new order with the patient profile. Look for medication duplication, drug class duplication, or other possible problems. If you discover problems, notify the pharmacist immediately before proceeding. Problems that may require a pharmacist's intervention include a potential adverse drug event, new prescription or nonprescription medication, and suspected drug misuse or nonadherence.

c. Enter the date, drug name, dosage form, dispensing quantity, directions for use, and number of refills, if any.

d. Enter the prescriber information and the initials of the technician and supervising pharmacist dispensing the medication. How this information gets entered may vary from pharmacy to pharmacy.

e. Enter the reimbursement mechanism or third-party payer information.

f. Enter other information as required by the pharmacy's policies and procedures.

B. DUR alerts

1. Pharmacy computer systems include automated DUR or DUE alerts to signal pharmacists and technicians to potential medication errors or problems, such as drug-drug interactions or adverse drug reactions.

   A DUR alert may appear during the order-entry process or when a prescription claim gets submitted electronically. Technicians should watch for DUR alerts and let the pharmacist know when one arises to ensure patient safety and appropriate medication use.

C. Verifying prescription validity

1. Technicians should watch for forged or invalid prescriptions, which happen most commonly with controlled substances. A forged prescription may:

   a. have an altered quantity, or
   b. be written on altered, invalid, or stolen prescription blanks

2. A prescription for a controlled substance must contain the prescriber's name, address, and Drug Enforcement Administration (DEA) number. The patient's name and address must also appear on the prescription.

3. If you question the validity of a prescription, verify the prescriber's DEA number. However, a prescription may still be invalid or forged even if the DEA number is valid.

   To verify a DEA number, use the following formula:

   Step 1: Add the 1st, 3rd, and 5th digits.
   Step 2: Add the 2nd, 4th, and 6th digits. Multiple this number by 2.
   Step 3: Add the two totals together.
   Step 4: The second digit in that total should equal the last digit in the DEA number (referred to as the "check digit").

Here is an example for DEA Number BG6125341:

Step 1: Add the 1st, 3rd, and 5th digits: 6 + 2 + 3 = 11
Step 2: Add the 2nd, 4th, and 6th digits, then multiple this number by 2: 1 + 5 + 4 = 10 x 2 = 20
Step 3: Add the two totals together: 20 + 11 = 31
Step 4: The second digit in that total should equal the last digit in the DEA number: The second digit in that total is "1," which equals the last digit in the DEA number, so this DEA number is valid.

If you suspect that a prescription is altered or invalid, alert the pharmacist and follow the pharmacy's policies and procedures. You may also need to notify the local narcotics office.

D. Processing investigational drug orders

1. Investigational drugs are prepared by pharmacists and technicians, following protocols for dispensing, recordkeeping, storage, and preparation. Investigational Drug Services, provided by pharmacy departments, oversees all of these activities. **Chapter 3** contains additional information on investigational drugs.

III. Selecting Appropriate Product(s) to Be Dispensed

A. Selecting the appropriate drug for a prescription or medication order

1. To minimize errors, you should fill prescriptions and medication orders from the original order. While filling the order, carefully check the information in the patient profile and on the prescription label to verify its accuracy against the original prescription/medication order. If you note a discrepancy or question, let the pharmacist know.

B. Selecting the product(s) to be dispensed. Prescriptions and medication orders may be written in two ways:

1. Generic drug name (drug's chemical name)

   a. When a pharmaceutical manufacturer's patent expires for a proprietary or brand-name drug, other companies may obtain approval from the Food and Drug Administration (FDA) to manufacture and market a generic product. Each pharmacy has different preferred manufacturing sources for generic drugs based on pricing and contracts.

      When a prescription or medication order is written generically, selecting which product to dispense usually depends on the preferred manufacturing source. **Chapter 1** details *therapeutic equivalence*, the process used to certify that a generic drug is equivalent to its brand counterpart.

2. Trade or brand name

   a. Appropriate methods for processing prescriptions and medication orders written as brand-name drugs depend on state laws, third-party payers, individual pharmacies or institutions, and other factors. In most cases, if a therapeutically equivalent generic product is available, it will be substituted for the brand-name drug.

      (1) Hospitals, health systems, and institutions. The *Pharmacy and Therapeutics Committee* usually develops the policies related to drug product use within the institution and creates formularies based on these decisions. A *formulary* or *preferred drug list* contains preferred or acceptable medications set by a payer or a specific institution.

      Formulary decisions may be driven by cost, drug effectiveness, or safety. The formulary restricts which drugs a physician may prescribe and gives the pharmacy department authority to substitute a generic equivalent for a trade-name product if available. As a result, when a medication order is written in trade-name terminology, the order is usually filled with the preferred generic equivalent. If no generic equivalent exists and the drug is on the formulary, the order is filled with the trade-name product.

      (2) Community and ambulatory pharmacies. Each pharmacy may set its own policies and procedures in addition to the preferred generics mentioned above. Most commonly, third-party payers dictate whether the prescription will be filled (some medications are not covered on a payer's formulary) and how they will be filled (trade name or generic). Most payers require generic substitution when available. If a generic equivalent is available, the technician or pharmacist will usually ask the patient or the patient's representative if he or she will accept a generic substitute. If the patient or patient's representative prefers the trade-name version not approved by his or her particular health insurance company, the patient will usually have to pay the price difference to the pharmacy.

C. Obtaining medications or devices from inventory. After determining the manufacturing source of the product(s) to be dispensed, obtain the medications or devices from inventory.

D. Calibrating equipment for preparing or compounding the prescription or medication order. As an important quality control measure and to ensure accuracy, pharmacies should regularly calibrate the equipment used for measuring or compounding prescriptions and medication orders. Each pharmacy department has policies and procedures that describe calibration methods and schedules to follow to ensure that equipment stays maintained on a routine basis.

IV. Preparing and Dispensing Medications to Fill Prescriptions and Medication Orders

A. Dispensing finished dosage forms

1. Measure or count finished dosage forms according to instructions on the original prescription or medication order. **Chapter 11** contains more information on avoiding medication errors in the dispensing process.

B. Calculations

1. At the direction of the pharmacist, the technician may help perform and/or verify pharmaceutical calculations. **Section VII** includes a thorough discussion of calculations.

C. Preparing intravenous admixtures and other sterile products

1. Preparation procedures for intravenous admixtures and other sterile products can be found in a variety of sources. **Sections IV and VII** provide more detail on these procedures.

D. Compounding medications for dispensing according to prescription formula or instructions

1. At the pharmacist's direction, technicians may help with the compounding function. **Sections IV and VII** contain more information on compounding.

E. Using appropriate computer-related technology to dispense medications

Some pharmacies or health systems use automated equipment to help prepare, deliver, and administer medication orders. For example, Baker cell systems can be programmed to count quantities of frequently dispensed medications stored in bulk. Other commonly used technology includes robotics, automated total parenteral nutrition preparation equipment, automated dispensing cabinets, and drug infusion pumps.

Technicians routinely use the following computer-related technology to assist in dispensing medications:

1. *Automated prescription-dispensing machines*. Technicians fill bins and program these machines to count quantities of frequently dispensed medications stored in bulk.

2. *Automated cart-fill machines*. These machines have cart drawers called *cassettes* that contain medications for a set time period (e.g., 24 hours) for a given patient. Technicians fill medication bins and the automated cart-fill machine fills the cassettes by pulling medication from the bins.

3. *Automated point-of-care dispensing machines* (e.g., Pyxis® machines). Nursing staff use these machines in the point-of-care area to obtain needed medications directly from the Pyxis® machine for administration to patients.

4. *Robots* or *robotic technology devices*. These devices also directly assist in delivering medications to patient-care areas in some institutions.

F. Recording preparation of medication in various dosage forms

1. Document information describing how the prescription was prepared on the prescription or medication order and on the patient profile.

G. Recording preparation of controlled substances for dispensing

1. By law, controlled substances require strict inventory control and documentation to record the dispensing of both established dosage forms and as ingredients of compounded preparations. **Chapter 3** details the recordkeeping requirements of controlled substances.

   The following information may be required to document the dispensing or use of controlled substances in preparing compounded products:

   a. Date the drug was removed from inventory

   b. Amount of drug that was removed from inventory

   c. How the drug was used (e.g., in the preparation of a cough syrup)

   d. Patient and auxiliary information

   e. Technician and pharmacist initials

V. Packaging Medications

A. Prescriptions

1. Prescription preparations are usually packaged according to the requirements of the specific drug and/or dosage form. Most preparations, regardless of dosage form, are packaged and dispensed in containers that protect the drug from light, which can hasten the degradation of drug products.

2. Certain drug products must be dispensed with special packaging requirements or in their original container. For example, some medications must be packaged from the manufacturer as unit-dose products to prevent accidental ingestion and poisoning, and must be dispensed in approved unit-dose packaging.

3. The *Poison Prevention Packaging Act of 1970* required most prescription and nonprescription drugs to be packaged in child-resistant containers.

B. Medication orders

1. Unit-dose packaging

   a. Unit-dose packaging is used for medications packaged individually (e.g., blister packing). This includes most drugs dispensed in the institutional setting. Unit-dose packaging may also be used to fill orders dispensed to other types of institutions, such as long-term care facilities or dialysis centers.

      When not commercially available, the pharmacy department may use special equipment to package "bulk" medications into unit-dose forms.

   b. Depending on the institution and the patient population, automated or remote dispensing or administration systems (e.g., Pyxis® cabinets, crash carts) may be used that require special packaging in the pharmacy. Technicians should familiarize themselves with the different dispensing technologies and requirements within their institution.

2. Multiple-dose packaging (or multi-dose packaging)

   a. Drugs may be dispensed in "bulk," which may include more than a single dosage and sometimes several days' supply of medication. Multiple-dose packaging is most commonly used for drugs not commercially available in unit-dose packaging and not used by the hospital in sufficient quantity to make repackaging into unit-dose forms feasible. These products will require labeling consistent with the requirements of prescription labels.

      (1) Single-day (24-hour) supply. The pharmacy department may dispense a 24-hour supply of the drug in a labeled prescription vial. This is most commonly used for oral dosage forms.

      (2) Multiple-day supply. For some dosage forms, it is not reasonable to attempt repackaging into a single-day supply (e.g., creams, ointments not available in unit-dose packages).

3. Packaging of sterile products

   a. Sterile products intended for intravenous or intramuscular injection usually get prepared by adding medications or nutrients to a sterile solution in the final container that will be aseptically sealed and dispensed. Sometimes, technicians need to transfer solutions through intravenous tubing to the final container. Some preparations require filtration to remove particles or ensure sterility. For example, liquid drug products from a glass ampule require needle filtration before use to remove any small glass particles in the liquid.

      The technician should become proficient in these techniques, be knowledgeable about the individual processes required for each medication, and follow all institutional policies and procedures for sterile products. Sterile compounding procedures are detailed in **Chapter 10**.

VI. Labeling Prescriptions and Medication Orders

A. Prescriptions. Label all prescriptions with the following information:

1. Name and address of pharmacy
2. Date the prescription was filled
3. Prescription number
4. Drug name (generic or trade), strength, and quantity
5. Directions for patient (administration route, schedule, duration)
6. Patient's name
7. Prescriber's name
8. Expiration date
9. Number of refills (if authorized)
10. Lot number
11. Pharmacist's initials
12. Auxiliary labels providing additional information on storage, administration guidelines (e.g., "Take with food"), cautions (e.g., "May cause drowsiness"), etc. Auxiliary label information may print automatically as part of the prescription label, or you may need to apply these labels individually to the bottle as small, colored stickers.
13. Other information required by state or federal laws
    a. Controlled substances
        (1) Federal transfer label

B. Medication orders

1. Unit-dose medication labels should contain the following information. Note that commercially available unit-dose products are already labeled by the manufacturer with the appropriate information, although auxiliary labels may be needed for some drugs.
    a. Drug name and strength
    b. Lot number

c. Expiration date

d. Directions for administration if necessary (e.g., for intramuscular injection only)

e. Auxiliary labels if necessary (e.g., storage, administration guidelines, cautions)

2. Multiple-dose package labels should include the following information:

a. Patient's name and room number

b. Drug name, strength, and quantity

c. Directions for administration

d. Lot number

e. Expiration date

f. Auxiliary labels if necessary (e.g., storage, administration guidelines, cautions)

3. Sterile product labels should contain the same information required on multiple-dose packages.

VII. Verifying the Accuracy of Dispensing and Labeling

A. Performing intermediate checks during the processing of the prescription/medication order

1. Performing intermediate checks is critical during the dispensing and labeling process. Technicians should pay attention to the details of the prescription/medication order, continually comparing the original order, label, patient profile, and the drug selected for accuracy throughout the dispensing process. Additional steps for avoiding errors are detailed in **Section V.**

2. Bar code technology

a. Pharmacies or health systems may utilize bar code technology to facilitate product selection and dispensing verification at different steps throughout the dispensing process. Bar code technology is linked to the patient, product, and prescription throughout the workflow process to help verify that the right drug is dispensed to the correct patient.

3. The technician may also need to verify the measurements, preparation, and/or packaging of medications produced by other technicians.

B. Pharmacist authorization

1. You must obtain and document authorization from the supervising pharmacist before dispensing prescriptions or medication orders.

C. Technician authorization

1. If allowed by law, the final check/verification of the prescription or medication order may be performed by a supervising technician (sometimes referred to as tech-check-tech).

VIII. Compiling Patient Information Materials

A. At the pharmacist's direction, the technician may need to collect supplemental patient information materials (e.g., patient package inserts [PPIs], computer-generated information, videos) for dispensing with the prescription/medication order.

IX. Delivering Medications to the Patient or the Patient's Representative

A. The technician should be familiar with the following functions related to the delivery of medications to patients. Specific policies and procedures governing these functions may vary, depending on the institution or pharmacy.

1. Storing medications prior to distribution

    a. The technician should know the pharmacy's policies regarding storage of medications prior to distribution and also understand which medications require special storage conditions (e.g., refrigeration).

2. Delivering medication to the patient or patient's representative

    a. Ambulatory/outpatient setting

        (1) In most states, technicians can offer the pharmacist consultation/counseling services required by OBRA '90 legislation. **Chapter 3** details this information.

    b. Institutional/inpatient setting

        (1) Place medication in the unit-dose cart.

        (2) Deliver medication to the patient-care unit.

        (3) Deliver medication according to any other institution-specific procedures or systems (e.g., crash cart stocking, automated dispensing cabinets).

    c. Pharmacy benefits management company or mail-order setting

        (1) These companies package and ship pharmaceuticals, durable and nondurable medical equipment, devices, and supplies (including hazardous substances and investigational products) directly to the patient/patient's representative.

3. Recording distribution of prescription medications

    a. Some pharmacies utilize bar code technology to record when a prescription is dispensed to the patient and distributed out of the pharmacy. Others may document this through signature of the patient/patient's representative when the medication gets picked up.

4. Recording distribution of controlled substances

    a. By law, controlled substances require strict inventory control and documentation to record dispensing as both established dosage forms and as ingredients of compounded preparations. **Chapter 3** details these requirements.

X. Providing Supplemental Information, as Indicated

A. The technician should ask all patients if they desire pharmacist counseling or consultation, consistent with OBRA '90 legislation. **Chapter 3** details this information.

B. At the pharmacist's direction, the technician may need to give the patient supplemental information materials along with the prescription/medication order.

1. Some drugs must be dispensed with a PPI or a medication guide according to FDA risk management requirements. In many cases, this supplemental information is included in the prescription packaging to facilitate distribution to patients. For example, the PPIs for estrogen-containing products are generally included inside the package; medication guides for many common drugs are glued to a stock bottle containing a 30-day supply so that they get dispensed along with the medication.

    Technicians should familiarize themselves with medications requiring supplemental information for patients and follow the pharmacy's policies and procedures for distributing these materials. **Chapter 4** contains more information on supplemental information requirements.

XI. Chapter Summary

A. Processing prescriptions and medication orders is a multifaceted operation requiring knowledge of many different aspects of pharmacy technician practice.

B. Technicians must pay strict attention to detail while performing multiple tasks, such as reviewing the patient profile; selecting, preparing, packaging, and labeling the appropriate product to fill the order; verifying the accuracy of dispensing and labeling through intermediate checks; calculating patient charges and obtaining compensation from third-party payers; and delivering the product and supplemental patient information to the patient or patient's representative.

XII. Questions for Discussion

A. Before the unit-dose system was developed, institutions typically dispensed a 5-day supply of each regular medication, packaged and labeled in a prescription vial. Discuss the advantages and disadvantages of each system.

B. What factors should you consider when selecting the appropriate product to dispense for a prescription/medication order?

C. Describe various types of packaging and discuss the advantages and disadvantages of each.

D. Describe steps technicians can take if they question the validity of a prescription.

E. Describe technologies related to the medication dispensing process. How do these impact patient safety and workflow in the pharmacy?

XIII. Sample Questions

1. Which of the following automated computer warnings alerts the pharmacist or technician to a potential problem with a prescription?

   a. FDA alerts
   b. DUR or DUE alerts
   c. PPI alerts
   d. Medication Guides

2. Which of the following is required on a controlled substance prescription?

   a. Prescriber's DEA number
   b. Brand name of prescribed drug
   c. Patient's diagnosis
   d. Prescriber's date of birth

3. Which of the following terms describes a list of preferred medications used at an institution or within a third-party payment system?

   a. formulary
   b. primary document
   c. medication guide
   d. Orange Book

4. Medications that require administration in individual doses need what type of packaging?

   a. bulk medication packaging
   b. multi-dose packaging
   c. unit-dose packaging
   d. in-stock medication packaging

5. Additional information about medication storage, administration, or cautions can be applied to the prescription bottle as:

   a. patient package insert
   b. self care labels
   c. drug info labels
   d. auxiliary labels

6. Which automated technology can be used to facilitate efficiency and safety in the medication dispensing process?

   a. automated dispensing cabinets
   b. Baker cells
   c. bar codes
   d. all of the above

7. Supplemental information that must be provided to the patient with some prescriptions as part of FDA risk management requirements is referred to as a:

   a. medication guide
   b. product labeling
   c. drug information handout
   d. patient information

8. Which of the following groups usually sets a hospital's formulary or preferred drug list?

   a. Food and Drug Administration
   b. Drug Enforcement Administration
   c. Pharmacy Governance Committee
   d. Pharmacy and Therapeutics Committee

The **Answer Key** appears in **Section VIII**.

Notes:

Chapter 8

Third-Party Billing Systems and Reimbursement

I. Key Terms and Concepts

A. A *health maintenance organization* (HMO) offers subscribers a range of medical services for a predetermined fee. In HMOs, patients receive care from a set network of physicians, pharmacies, and other providers.

B. A *preferred provider organization* (PPO) also offers subscribers a range of medical services for a predetermined fee. However, patients may receive care from a wider range of providers than with HMOs. In PPOs, the patient's out-of-pocket costs are less with preferred providers and increase with nonpreferred providers.

C. A *pharmacy benefits manager* (PBM) is a third-party administrator of prescription drug programs that processes and pays prescription drug claims; develops and maintains formularies; and contracts with pharmacies.

D. *Prior authorization* by the insurer may be needed for a patient to receive some drug products or services.

E. A *pharmacy audit* of billing practices may be conducted to verify compliance with third-party requirements.

II. Billing and Reimbursement Terminology

A. *Copayment* – A copayment is the amount the patient pays for a prescription. This amount is set by the patient's prescription insurer as either a fixed dollar amount or a percentage of the total prescription cost. This amount may also vary based on the drug's formulary status or other factors.

B. *Deductible* – A deductible is a predetermined amount that the patient must pay during each benefit period before insurance benefits are administered.

C. *HMO* – An HMO offers subscribers a range of medical services for a predetermined fee. In HMOs, patients receive care from a set network of physicians, pharmacies, and other providers.

D. *PPO* – In a PPO, subscribers receive a range of medical services for a predetermined fee. However, patients may receive care from a wider range of providers than with HMOs. In PPOs, the patient's out-of-pocket costs are less with preferred providers and increase with nonpreferred providers.

E. *PBM* – The PBM is a third-party administrator of prescription drug programs that processes and pays prescription drug claims; develops and maintains formularies; and contracts with pharmacies.

III. Methods of Payment

A. The majority of prescriptions or medication orders get paid for by one of the following methods:

1. Direct payment (also referred to as self-pay or "cash" payment)

   a. The patient pays all prescription drug costs out of pocket, with no insurance.

   b. Patients may have a "prescription discount card" that is not an insurance card but provides reduced prices for some medications through a group membership, purchase, etc.

2. Reimbursement from a government program

   a. *Medicaid* is federally funded but administered individually by each state. Medicaid bases eligibility on financial need. States determine formulary and copayment amounts, and not all drugs are covered.

   b. *Medicare* is a federally funded program administered by the Centers for Medicare and Medicaid Services for individuals over age 65, disabled patients under age 65, and patients with kidney disease. Medicare Part D provides prescription drug coverage through contracts with PBMs and other prescription insurance providers to coordinate reimbursement.

3. Reimbursement from a nongovernmental payer (also referred to as a "private plan"), such as an HMO, PBM, or other prescription insurance company, the patient's employer, etc.

4. Patient assistance programs or coupons

   a. Some drug manufacturers offer assistance programs for patients with special financial needs or those who cannot afford their medications. Patients may present a special prescription card issued by the manufacturer.

   b. Drug manufacturers may also offer coupons or vouchers processed as a prescription card that decrease costs for a limited number of fills of a brand-name medication.

5. Workers' compensation

   a. Compensation for medications used to treat work-related injuries is provided through workers' compensation. Billing procedures vary, but claims may be billed to the employer directly, through an intermediary, or to the state bureau of workers' compensation.

IV. Determining Charges and Obtaining Compensation for Services

A. Calculating charges

   1. Charges for prescriptions and medication orders vary depending on a specific pharmacy department's policies and third-party reimbursement plans. **Chapter 19** provides a review of calculations related to pricing prescriptions.

B. Communicating with third-party payers to determine or verify coverage

   1. Patients will usually present to an outpatient or community pharmacy with a prescription card. The technician may need to contact third-party payers to verify the patient's eligibility for coverage. This communication may be done electronically through the pharmacy computer system or by telephone directly to the third-party payer.

C. Obtaining compensation

   1. Community pharmacy/outpatient setting

      a. Reimbursement from third-party payers

         (1) For patients covered by third-party plans in the outpatient or community pharmacy setting, technicians will usually submit an electronic claim via the pharmacy computer system to the company providing prescription benefit coverage for the patient. A response is quickly received in the pharmacy computer system detailing whether the product is covered for that patient, what the reimbursement from the third-party payer will be, what the patient's portion of the cost is, and any other required details.

      b. Payment from the patient or patient's representative

         (1) When patients or their representatives pick up their medication in the community pharmacy or outpatient setting, they will pay their required payment (copayment) specified by the third-party payer to receive their medication.

   2. Institutional/inpatient setting

      a. Patient billing

         (1) The pharmacy technician may need to bill drug charges to the patient's account. Direct billing to patients and third-party payers is usually done by the institution's accounting department and does not involve direct billing by the technician in the pharmacy department.

V. Resolving Third-Party Problems

A. The pharmacy technician may need to communicate with third-party payers to resolve common payment issues, such as:

1. Prior Authorizations ("prior auths") – the technician may need to contact the physician or third-party payers for prior approval of nonformulary drugs and supplies.

2. Rejected Claims – the technician may need to identify and resolve problems with rejected claims (e.g., incorrect days' supply, incorrect patient identification number, exceeded plan limits).

VI. Preventing Fraud, Waste, and Abuse

A. Pharmacy technicians should understand the necessary steps to prevent fraud, waste, and abuse with any third-party payer system. This can occur when a pharmacy bills a third-party payer for a product or service that was not provided. Examples include:

1. Billing for medications not dispensed

2. "Partial fills," in which the pharmacy bills for the full amount but the patient receives only a portion of the prescription

3. Billing for brand-name products when the generic is dispensed

B. A PBM or third-party payer may conduct a pharmacy audit to evaluate third-party claims or billing procedures for compliance with billing requirements. In the event of an audit, pharmacy technicians should make sure they understand the different requirements of third-party payers for documentation and plan limits.

VII. Chapter Summary

A. Reimbursement for prescriptions and medication orders is a multifaceted operation requiring knowledge of many different aspects of medical and pharmacy care.

B. Patients may pay for prescriptions and medication orders in many different ways. The pharmacy technician plays an important role in processing payments and helping patients get access to needed medications.

C. Technicians should understand the different requirements of third-party payers for documentation and plan limits to ensure compliance and prevent fraud, waste, and abuse.

VIII. Questions for Discussion

A. Describe different prescription payment methods. What are the advantages and disadvantages of each?

B. Discuss methods for preventing pharmacy fraud with third-party payment systems.

C. What is the difference between a PBM and an HMO?

D. What are the differences between Medicare and Medicaid? How do these differences impact patients' prescription payment in the pharmacy?

IX. Sample Questions

1. Subscribers pay a predetermined fee for a range of medical services and are eligible to receive care from a set network of providers in which of the following:

    a. HMO
    b. PBM
    c. PPO
    d. CMS

2. Which of the following terms refers to a predetermined dollar amount that the patient must pay during each benefit period before insurance benefits are administered?

    a. copay
    b. coupon
    c. payment
    d. deductible

3. Patients with financial needs may be eligible for which program administered by the drug manufacturer?

    a. Medicare
    b. Patient assistance programs
    c. Financial drug programs
    d. Workers' compensation

4. Which of the following is an example of fraud, waste, and abuse that may occur with prescription billing?

    a. Billing for medications not dispensed
    b. Dispensing a partial fill, but billing for the full prescription
    c. Billing for name-brand product when the generic is dispensed
    d. All of the above

5. Which of the following is a federally funded program for individuals over age 65, disabled patients under age 65, and patients with kidney disease?

   a. Medicaid
   b. PBM
   c. Medicare
   d. CMS

6. Which portion of Medicare is responsible for prescription drug coverage?

   a. Medicare Part A
   b. Medicare Part B
   c. Medicare Part C
   d. Medicare Part D

The **Answer Key** appears in **Section VIII**.

Notes:

Section IV

Pharmacy Compounding

Kristin W. Weitzel

Section IV details activities related to pharmacy compounding, including:

- aseptic preparation of sterile products
- nonsterile compounding processes
- selection and use of compounding equipment and supplies
- infection control steps and personal protective equipment

Chapter 9

Nonsterile Compounding

I. Key Terms and Concepts

A. *United States Pharmacopeia (USP) Chapter <795>* provides standards for nonsterile compounding of pharmaceutical products.

B. *Compounding* is the act or process of combining two or more drug products or chemicals into a single preparation.

C. *Nonsterile products* include solutions, suspensions, ointments, creams, powders, suppositories, tablets, or capsules that are prepared for external or oral use.

D. *Trituration* uses a mortar and pestle to grind a drug solid to reduce particle size, or to mix two or more solids together.

E. *Levigation* disperses a drug solid in a small amount of mineral oil, glycerin, or other liquid before incorporating it into a compounding base, such as an ointment.

F. *Geometric dilution* is a method for mixing a small amount of a potent drug with a large amount of a nonpotent or inactive compound.

II. Standards and Regulation of Nonsterile Compounding

A. Compounding standards are set by the USP. USP Chapter <795> provides standards for nonsterile compounding of pharmaceutical products and divides nonsterile compounding into three categories:

1. *Simple compounding* is defined by USP as making a preparation according to an established monograph or formula and applying published stability data for that specific formulation, or reconstituting or manipulating commercial products according to manufacturer instructions (e.g., reconstitution of an antibiotic suspension).

2. *Moderate compounding* is defined by USP as making preparations that require special calculations or procedures to determine the amount of each component per preparation or dosage unit or making a preparation that does not have published stability data for that specific formulation (e.g., mixing two or more creams together when the stability of the final product is unknown).

3. *Complex compounding*, as defined by USP, requires advanced training and special equipment, preparation environment, and procedures (e.g., making transdermal patches).

   Pharmacies are regulated by state boards of pharmacies, which may choose to adopt USP standards. Individual institutions or institutional accrediting bodies may also adopt or endorse USP quality standards for nonsterile compounding.

III. Nonsterile Compounding Equipment

A. Prescription balance or scale for weighing ingredients

1. All pharmacies must have a prescription balance to weigh small quantities of ingredients.

2. To control quality and ensure accuracy, pharmacies should regularly calibrate equipment used for measuring or compounding, such as prescription balances. Pharmacy departments have policies and procedures that describe calibration methods and schedules to follow to ensure that equipment gets maintained on a routine basis.

B. Graduated cylinder or other containers for measuring liquids accurately

1. Size – the liquid you will measure should fill at least 20% of the graduated cylinder. For example, to measure a volume of 3 mL, you would use a 10 mL graduated cylinder instead of a 100 mL graduated cylinder.

C. Compounding equipment, such as:

1. Mortars and pestles (both glass and wood)

2. Metal spatulas for mixing powders into ointments or creams

3. Ointment slab, ointment papers, or pill tiles as a work surface for mixing ingredients

4. Funnels, filter paper, beakers, glass stirring rods, and a heat source

D. Preventing and treating unintended exposure to hazardous substances

1. Nonsterile compounding may require handling of hazardous drugs or other substances. In these cases, the compounding equipment should include supplies and information appropriate for managing hazardous substances (e.g., eyewash kit, spill kit, Material Safety Data Sheets). **Chapter 13** contains more information on storage, handling, and disposal of hazardous drug substances.

IV. Nonsterile Compounding Processes

A. At the pharmacist's direction, technicians may need to assist in the compounding function. Compounds are generally prepared according to a written prescription or an existing formula. **Section VII** discusses the calculations related to compounding preparations.

B. Techniques commonly used to mix ingredients together in the nonsterile compounding process include:

1. *Trituration*: using a mortar and pestle to grind a drug solid to reduce particle size, or to mix two or more solids together.

2. *Levigation*: dispersing a drug solid in a small amount of mineral oil, glycerin, or other liquid before incorporating it into a compounding base, such as an ointment.

3. *Geometric dilution*: method for mixing a small amount of a potent drug with a large amount of a nonpotent or inactive compound.

C. Bulk compounding

1. Many commercially unavailable compounds are prescribed and dispensed on a regular basis.

   To save time, many pharmacies prepare or *bulk compound* large quantities of frequently prescribed medications in advance. Technicians should learn the pharmacy's policies and procedures for bulk compounding to prevent shortages and reduce waste.

D. Compounding records

1. Recordkeeping requirements differ among pharmacies and states, but in general, you will need to keep a compounding record whenever you prepare an individual or bulk compound. Pharmacies may keep records in a separate compounding log or in inventory records. This record may include:

   a. Identification of the technician and/or pharmacist who prepared the product

   b. Drug name, strength, dosage form, and quantity used

   c. Names, manufacturers, lot numbers, and quantities of all ingredients

   d. Mixing order, formula, and procedures used

   e. Storage information

   f. Date the compound was prepared

   g. Pharmacy lot number for bulk compounded products

V. Packaging and Storage of Compounded Nonsterile Products

A. Beyond-use dating

1. All compounded nonsterile products get assigned a *beyond-use date,* after which the compounded product should not be used. The beyond-use date differs from the expiration dates of the individual ingredients and is based on chemical and physical stability, compatibility, microbial growth potential, and other factors.

2. USP Chapter <795> provides specific guidance to determine beyond-use dates for nonsterile compounds. Pharmacies may follow these or other guidelines but should have written policies and procedures in place documenting beyond-use dating procedures for compounded products.

B. Storage areas

1. Storage areas for prepared nonsterile compounds must be monitored to ensure compliance with storage requirements. If you discover a product has been stored outside of recommended storage requirements, you may need to discard it.

2. Pharmacies should verify and log temperature measurements in refrigerators, freezers, or other special storage enclosures daily. In addition, pharmacy personnel should log the temperature each time they enter or remove a product from the storage container. **Chapter 13** details standard storage temperature requirements, and **Chapter 16** provides temperature conversion formulas.

VI. Chapter Summary

A. Preparing nonsterile compounded products requires the technician to master compounding techniques and understand the processes and requirements specific to each type of compounding.

B. At the pharmacist's direction, technicians may need to assist in the compounding function. Technicians must pay strict attention to detail while performing compounding procedures to ensure the appropriate techniques and ingredients are used.

C. Technicians responsible for nonsterile compounding must understand USP Chapter <795> requirements, as well as the policies and procedures regarding preparation, storage, labeling, and recordkeeping requirements for nonsterile compounded products.

VII. Questions for Discussion

A. What is USP Chapter <795> and what is its role in setting standards for nonsterile compounding in pharmacies?

B. Describe the equipment and common techniques and processes used to prepare nonsterile compounded products.

C. Discuss beyond-use dating. What factors should you consider in setting beyond-use dates for nonsterile compounded products?

D. Describe recordkeeping requirements for nonsterile compounded products.

VIII. Sample Questions

1. The standards for nonsterile compounding of pharmaceutical products are outlined in:

   a. USP Chapter <795>
   b. OSHA
   c. USP Chapter <797>
   d. NIOSH

2. Using a mortar and pestle to grind a drug solid to reduce particle size is called:

   a. levigation
   b. trituration
   c. sterilization
   d. powdering

3. Which of the following tools is commonly used to measure liquids for nonsterile compounding?

   a. prescription balance
   b. calibrator
   c. graduated cylinder
   d. funnel

4. Which of the following pieces of equipment is especially important when preparing compounds that contain hazardous drugs or other substances?

   a. ointment slab
   b. mortar and pestle
   c. eyewash kit
   d. prescription balance

5. Preparing a large quantity of a compound in advance in anticipation of future prescriptions is called:

   a. bulk compounding
   b. nonsterile compounding
   c. sterile compounding
   d. extemporaneous compounding

6. Records for compounded substances will generally include:

   a. lot numbers of all ingredients
   b. storage information
   c. identification of individual preparing the compound
   d. all of the above

7. The date after which a compounded product should not be used is the:

   a. expiration date
   b. nonuse date
   c. compound date
   d. beyond-use date

The **Answer Key** appears in **Section VIII**.

Notes:

Chapter 10

Sterile Compounding

I. Key Terms and Concepts

A. *United States Pharmacopeia (USP) Chapter <797>* provides standards for sterile compounding of pharmaceutical products.

B. *Sterile* products must be *aseptic*, free from pathogenic microorganisms, and contain no bacterial or viral contaminants.

C. *Intravenous* (IV) *admixtures* are IV solutions compounded with two or more ingredients (e.g., one or more additives mixed with the primary IV solution).

D. *Laminar airflow hoods* are used to prevent contamination by microorganisms when preparing sterile products. These hoods can filter air horizontally or vertically. *Horizontal airflow hoods* are used to prepare most products. *Vertical airflow hoods* are used to protect the operator from exposure to harmful agents when preparing cytotoxic drugs.

E. *Cytotoxic agents* or *cytotoxins* are drugs that are "toxic" to cells of susceptible organs. Cytotoxic agents commonly treat many forms of cancer (neoplasms).

F. *Antineoplastic agents* refer to specialized drugs used to treat cancers.

G. *Personal protective equipment* (PPE) refers to special equipment (e.g., gloves) and procedures for handling or compounding hazardous drugs.

II. Standards and Regulation of Sterile Compounding

A. Sterile compounding standards are set by the USP. USP Chapter <797> provides standards for sterile compounding of pharmaceutical products.

Pharmacies are regulated by state boards of pharmacies, which may choose to adopt USP standards. Individual institutions or institutional accrediting bodies may also adopt or endorse USP quality standards for sterile compounding.

B. Occupational Safety and Health Administration (OSHA) and National Institute for Occupational Safety and Health (NIOSH) develop guidelines and regulations related to sterile compounding, hazardous drug handling, and use of PPE to ensure workplace safety.

III. Preparing Intravenous Admixtures and Other Sterile Products

Technicians may help prepare sterile IV fluids containing drugs, vitamins, or other nutrients for hospital inpatients or outpatients.

A. Aseptic (sterile) technique
Compounding IV solutions, other types of injections (intramuscular, subcutaneous, etc.), ophthalmic and otic products, and preparations that will be instilled directly into the patient's body tissues (e.g., irrigation solutions) requires strict adherence to *aseptic technique* to prevent contamination by microorganisms.

1. Each institution and ambulatory pharmacy has written policies describing the proper use of aseptic technique. This type of compounding usually takes place in a separate sterile compounding room or in a specially designated area in the pharmacy. Correct use of aseptic technique involves proper attire, efficient hand washing, sterilization of the compounding surface (horizontal or vertical laminar airflow hood), aseptic preparation of the sterile products, and sterile maintenance of the compounding area.

a. Proper attire for sterile technique

(1) Proper attire for pharmacists and technicians preparing sterile products consists of a sterile gown, sterile gloves, a face mask to cover the nose and mouth, and a cap to contain and cover the hair.

b. Hand washing

(1) Before preparing sterile products, technicians must wash their hands thoroughly using chlorhexidine or another disinfectant.

c. Sterilization of the compounding surface

(1) The sterilizing agent may vary by institution or pharmacy. Ethyl alcohol (ethanol) and isopropyl alcohol (isopropanol or "rubbing alcohol") are the most commonly used agents. To sterilize the compounding surface, pour alcohol in a thick layer on the hood surface, wipe down the surface with sterile gauze from back to front, and leave it wet until the alcohol evaporates. Leaving the compounding surface wet allows enough time for the alcohol to kill microorganisms that may live on the surface.

d. Sterilization of the injection sites on the additive containers

(1) Similarly, saturate the injection site on the additive vial with an alcohol preparation. Then, wipe the site with sterile gauze to clean the area where the needle gets inserted to inject, reconstitute, and withdraw the additive.

e. Maintaining the sterility of aseptic preparation materials

(1) While preparing aseptic products, take care to keep all surfaces and materials sterile. Make sure that they do not come into contact with other surfaces that may not be sterile, or surfaces that may be contaminated with other medications or substances.

f. Infection control standards

(1) The sterile compounding room or area must be scrupulously and continually maintained to ensure that all products are prepared in a completely aseptic environment. Pharmacies must conduct mandatory periodic tests to ensure that this area is properly maintained and contamination-free.

g. Preventing and treating unintended exposure to hazardous substances

(1) Sterile compounding may require handling hazardous drugs or other substances. In these cases, the compounding equipment should include supplies and information appropriate for managing hazardous substances (e.g., eyewash kit, spill kit, Material Safety Data Sheets). **Chapter 13** contains more information on storage, handling, and disposal of hazardous drug substances.

B. Compounding sterile preparations

1. Procedures for preparing IV admixtures and other sterile products can be found in a variety of sources. **Section VII** details calculations related to the preparation of IV solutions.

2. Reconstitution

a. Many drugs are stored in the pharmacy as sterile powders that require reconstitution. Using aseptic technique, inject an appropriate amount of diluent (most commonly normal saline) into a vial for reconstitution. Then, shake the container and leave it on the hood surface until every particle of the powder has dissolved and the resultant solution becomes clear. Then, withdraw the solution from the vial and inject it into a larger volume of sterile solution. In some instances, the medication will be withdrawn and dispensed in a labeled syringe that is injected directly into the patient, or into another IV the patient is receiving.

3. Ampules

    a. *Ampules* are sealed glass containers that hold a small amount of drug. When obtaining drug from an ampule, first wipe the neck with an alcohol swab. Then, wrap the neck with gauze and break it. To avoid transferring glass fragments with the drug solution, use a filter needle to withdraw the solution. Then, exchange the old filter needle for a new filter needle, and transfer the liquid to the final container.

4. Preventing cross-contamination

    a. While aseptic technique prevents bacterial contamination, it also guards against cross-contamination between two or more drugs. This prevents serious and potentially fatal allergic reactions. With aseptic technique, the syringe used to dilute or withdraw one medication is never used to dilute or withdraw another drug.

       Similarly, materials used in the compounding of one drug must not touch containers or other materials used to prepare a different medication.

5. Incompatibility

    a. An *incompatibility* can occur when one drug is mixed with another and the product is unsuitable, because of physical or chemical changes such as drug precipitation. After compounding a sterile product, technicians should carefully inspect drug contents for particulate matter or other signs of incompatibility.

IV. Packaging and Storage of Compounded Sterile Products

A. Beyond-use dating

1. All pharmacies assign compounded sterile products a *beyond-use date*, after which the compounded product should not be used. The beyond-use date differs from the expiration dates of the individual ingredients and is based on chemical and physical stability, compatibility, microbial growth potential, and other factors.

2. USP Chapter <797> provides specific guidelines on determining beyond-use dates for sterile compounds. Pharmacies may follow these or other guidelines but should have written policies and procedures in place documenting beyond-use dating procedures for compounded sterile products.

B. Packaging sterile products

1. Sterile products intended for IV or intramuscular injection are usually prepared by adding medications or nutrients to a sterile solution in the final container that will be aseptically sealed and dispensed. Sometimes, solutions must be transferred through IV tubing to the final container. A few preparations must be filtered before dispensing.

Technicians should master these techniques and learn the individual processes required for each medication.

C. Storage areas

1. Carefully monitor storage areas for compounded sterile products to ensure strict compliance with storage requirements. If you discover a product has been stored outside of recommended storage requirements, you may need to discard it.

2. Verify and log temperature measurements in refrigerators, freezers, or other special storage enclosures daily. In addition, log the temperature each time you enter or remove a product from the storage container. **Chapter 13** details standard storage temperature requirements, and **Chapter 16** provides temperature conversion formulas.

V. Chemotherapeutic Products

A. *Chemotherapy* most commonly describes drugs that kill causative organisms, such as cancer cells. Chemotherapeutic agents may be toxic at any exposure level, and technicians need to take special precautions when preparing sterile chemotherapeutic products.

B. Most sterile products are prepared in a *horizontal* laminar airflow hood that directs filtered air horizontally toward the operator or technician to protect against contamination by microorganisms. Some chemotherapeutic agents used to treat cancer (neoplasms) are cytotoxic and can be hazardous to the operator. For this reason, these agents are prepared in a *vertical* laminar airflow hood (biological safety cabinet), which directs filtered air vertically (from top to bottom of the hood) to protect the operator from possible adverse effects that may occur from exposure to these agents.

C. Certain individuals should not work with chemotherapeutic drugs:

1. Pregnant or lactating women

2. Male or female staff who are actively trying to conceive a child

3. Personnel with a medical condition that may prohibit them from handling cytotoxic drugs

4. Personnel who fail to meet competency requirements

D. Technicians must establish competency to handle and prepare cytotoxic drugs.

1. Technicians handling cytoxic drugs must complete training in accordance with the institution's guidelines/protocols.

2. Technicians must demonstrate competency through written, oral, and/or practical testing.

E. Technicians should use PPE and take special precautions when handling any hazardous drug, including chemotherapeutic agents.

1. Technicians can be exposed to hazardous products through inhalation of drug aerosols, droplets, or particles; absorption through skin or eye contact; or ingestion through contact with contaminated food or food containers.

2. PPE

   a. Because powder may absorb the cytotoxic agent, use gloves without powder. Change gloves regularly or after a tear, spill, or puncture. Technicians working in chemo-only areas should also change gloves hourly or sooner, as needed.

   b. Technicians may also need to use gowns, masks, eye protectors, caps, sleeve, and shoe covers, depending on the practice site and extent of exposure. Each facility will have specific practice and procedural guidelines.

F. Prepare and maintain the work area and waste disposal

1. Restrict the preparation or work area where chemotherapeutic drugs are stored or prepared to authorized personnel only. Prohibit storing food, eating, and drinking in this area.

2. Do not remove apparel from the preparation area. Dispose of used apparel according to the practice site's hazardous waste disposal procedures.

3. Handle liquid spills according to the practice facility's policies and procedures.

4. Dispose of waste from these agents in puncture-proof cytotoxic waste containers, including cotton from bottles, pads used to wipe surfaces, gloves, bottles, and vials. Clearly label the disposal container as cytotoxic waste. **Chapter 13** contains more information on storage, handling, and disposal of hazardous drug substances.

VI. Other Special Products and Procedures

A. Enteral products

1. Enteral products are nutritional formulations that substitute for food in patients who are unable to eat. Patients receive nutrition through a feeding tube that enters the gastrointestinal tract through the esophageal route or through a surgically implanted port.

2. Most enteral products are manufactured and ready for use. If a commercially unavailable formulation is needed, the technician may need to calculate and compound a sterile formulation.

B. Specialized procedures

1. Some sterile compounded formulations require additional precautions or procedures such as ophthalmic products, agents for epidural injection, or agents prepared for a specific manufacturer delivery device. Technicians should learn specialized procedures required in their institution.

VII. Chapter Summary

A. Technicians responsible for sterile compounding must understand USP Chapter <797> requirements and workplace safety regulations regarding handling and disposal of hazardous drugs to maintain sterility and avoid toxicity.

B. Preparation of sterile products and admixtures requires the technician to master aseptic technique and learn about processes and requirements specific to each medication.

C. Technicians should learn infection control and aseptic technique requirements specific to their institution.

D. To ensure safety in the sterile compounding process, technicians should handle chemotherapeutic agents strictly according to policies and procedures.

VIII. Questions for Discussion

A. What is USP Chapter <797> and what is its role in setting standards for sterile compounding in pharmacies?

B. Describe aseptic technique and processes used to prepare sterile products.

C. Why do chemotherapy drugs require special handling?

D. What types of protection should technicians use when handling cytotoxic agents?

E. Why are powder-free gloves preferred when handling cytotoxic drugs?

IX. Sample Questions

1. The standards for sterile compounding of pharmaceutical products are outlined in:

   a. USP Chapter <795>
   b. OSHA
   c. USP Chapter <797>
   d. NIOSH

2. Chemotherapy agents are compounded using a:

   a. vertical airflow hood
   b. horizontal airflow hood
   c. cytotoxic hood
   d. neoplasm hood

3. Using aseptic technique in sterile compounding:

    a. avoids drug interactions
    b. prevents microbial contamination
    c. decreases costs
    d. increases volume of orders filled per day

4. The process of adding a diluent to a sterile powder to create a solution is called:

    a. punching
    b. triturating
    c. mixing
    d. reconstituting

5. If penicillin is mistakenly introduced into a heparin solution after a syringe is reused during the compounding process, what has occurred?

    a. infection
    b. cross-contamination
    c. meningitis
    d. single-source contamination

6. Which group of individuals should not handle chemotherapeutic drugs?

    a. pregnant females
    b. breastfeeding mothers
    c. men trying to conceive a child
    d. all of the above

7. The acronym PPE refers to which of the following?

    a. pharmacy personnel exposure
    b. pharmacy protection effect
    c. personal protective equipment
    d. personal pharmacy executive

8. Which term refers to the time after which a compounded product should not be used?

    a. manufacturer's expiration date
    b. unit of use
    c. beyond-use date
    d. exposure date

9. A normal saline solution is mixed with another injectable drug for IV administration. After mixing, the technician notices that a precipitate crystal has formed that will not dissolve. What is most likely causing this?

   a. poor aseptic technique
   b. incompatibility of saline solution and the injectable drug
   c. overheating the compounded solution
   d. using out-of-date products

10. A nutritional formulation that substitutes for food in a patient who is unable to eat is a/an:

    a. enteral product
    b. chemotherapeutic agent
    c. antineoplastic product
    d. cytotoxic agent

The **Answer Key** appears in **Section VIII**.

Notes:

Section V

Medication Safety and Pharmacy Quality Assurance

Kristin W. Weitzel

Section V outlines activities related to ensuring medication safety and maintaining quality in the pharmacy practice, including:

- error prevention steps and common safety strategies
- issues requiring pharmacist intervention
- risk management strategies and error reporting procedures
- quality assurance practices for medication and inventory control systems

Chapter 11

Avoiding Medication Errors to Improve Patient Safety

I. Key Terms and Concepts

A. A *medication error* includes any preventable event that may cause or lead to inappropriate medication use or patient harm, while the health care professional, patient, or consumer has control of the medication.

B. A *high-alert medication* has a high risk of causing injury if involved in an error.

C. A *system-based cause* of a medication error is a factor common to a health care, pharmacy, or patient care system that increases the likelihood of an error.

D. Technicians can report medication errors externally to the *Institute for Safe Medication Practices* (ISMP) *Medication Errors Reporting Program* (MERP).

E. Technicians can report serious adverse drug events, potential and actual product use errors, and product quality problems to the *FDA MedWatch* program.

II. Causes of Medication Errors

A. A medication error is defined as "any preventable event that may cause or lead to inappropriate medication use or patient harm, while the medication is in the control of the health care professional, patient, or consumer. Such events may be related to professional practice, health care products, procedures, and systems including: prescribing; order communication; product labeling, packaging and nomenclature; compounding; dispensing; distribution; administration; education; monitoring; and use."

B. Many medication errors occur because of individual causes. Staying aware of common causes of errors can help technicians improve safety in the pharmacy.

   1. Look-alike and sound-alike medications such as Adderall and Inderal, bupropion and buspirone, Celebrex and Celexa, guanfacine and guaifenesin, Klonopin and clonidine, etc., contribute to confusion. To avoid mix-ups, technicians should stay alert for medications with names that look and sound alike. A listing of drug names that are often confused is available at https://www.ismp.org/tools/confuseddrugnames.pdf.

2. Abbreviations contribute to many medication errors. Technicians may misinterpret abbreviations because of poor handwriting or confusion with a similar abbreviation. For example, "HS" may refer to "at bedtime" or "half-strength;" the abbreviation "*u*" for units can be mistaken for a numeric "four," causing a dose error. ISMP's listing of error-prone abbreviations, symbols, and dose designations is available at http://www.ismp.org/tools/errorproneabbreviations.pdf.

3. Leading or trailing zeroes can lead to a 10-fold over- or underdose. For example, if a warfarin dose for "1 mg" is written as "1.0" mg with a trailing zero, it can accidentally be read as "10 mg." Or, if "0.5 mg" is written as ".5 mg," this could lead to a 10-fold overdose if "5 mg" is mistakenly dispensed.

C. Medication errors may also result from *system-based* causes, or factors common to a specific health care or pharmacy system that increase the likelihood of an error.

Common system-based causes of errors include:

1. Lack of information about the patient or the medication

2. Unsafe drug storage or distribution

3. Environmental patterns (e.g., work environment) and unsafe staffing patterns

4. Inadequate staff orientation, training, education, supervision, or competency validation

5. Inadequate patient education

III. Preventing Medication Errors

A. The Five "Rights" of Safe Medication Use

Health care providers can use *the five rights of safe medication use* to help avoid errors. This system helps to ensure that the:

1. right drug is administered to the
2. right patient at the
3. right time in the
4. right dose by the
5. right route of administration.

Technicians should learn the five rights of safe medication use and other error prevention practices used in their pharmacy.

B. Separating inventory or using special tags or markers on shelves to highlight error-prone drugs can help avoid potential errors. For example, some pharmacies store drugs with names that look alike or sound alike separately from each other to prevent mix-ups.

C. Some manufacturers use *tall-man lettering* to show differences between drugs that commonly get confused for one another. For example, stock bottle labels reading "HydrALAzine" and "HydrOXYzine" highlight the differences between these otherwise similarly packaged and named generic drugs.

D. Many institutions employ *"Do Not Use" lists* to limit unsafe prescription writing and dispensing practices. For example, institutions may prohibit the use of error-prone abbreviations or leading and trailing zeros when writing out numbers. The Joint Commission created a list of "Do Not Use" abbreviations in 2004 for accredited organizations, which can be accessed at http://www.jointcommission.org/assets/1/18/Do_Not_Use_List.pdf.

E. A *high-alert medication* has a high risk of causing injury when involved in an error. Special storage or dispensing procedures for high-alert medications such as warfarin, insulin, or injectable potassium products can increase safety. For example, most hospitals that dispense the very concentrated U-500 insulin store it in a separate area and dispense it using special procedures. A medication error with this high-alert medication would result in a 5-fold insulin overdose and a high likelihood of dangerously low blood sugar and death. ISMP's list of high-alert medications is available at http://www.ismp.org/tools/highalertmedications.pdf.

F. *Electronic prescribing* and *computerized physician order entry* have both been shown to decrease medication errors caused by poor handwriting. However, these systems can introduce other types of errors, such as the physician or pharmacist selecting the wrong drug or dose from a computer drop-down menu.

G. *Bar code technology* decreases errors by providing a "check system" within the dispensing process to ensure the right product is matched consistently with the right prescription and patient.

H. Some populations, such as pediatrics and older adults, are at higher risk for medication errors. To prevent errors, technicians should learn the special dispensing requirements or checks in place for these population groups. For example, pharmacies that compound or dispense small volume products for premature infants use special labeling to differentiate these from adult-strength formulations.

I. In addition to those previously listed, technicians can find resources for preventing medication errors from the ISMP website (www.ismp.org), Food and Drug Administration (FDA) website (www.fda.gov), pharmacy and pharmacy technician associations, employer training, and continuing education programs. Many states require technicians to complete periodic medication error continuing education to obtain license renewal.

IV. Documenting and Reporting Medication Errors

A. If a medication error occurs, pharmacy technicians should follow their employer's documentation, reporting, and risk management procedures. Technicians should understand rules regarding documenting patient records and communicating with patients.

B. In most cases, technicians should also report medication errors or adverse events externally. National organizations track medication errors or adverse events to help increase awareness and implement changes to prevent future problems.

C. Organizations that track medication errors, adverse events, and problems with drug integrity include:

1. The ISMP MERP provides data on medication errors to FDA, regulatory and accrediting agencies, and manufacturers to promote changes that can improve patient safety.

   Technicians can report errors confidentially and anonymously at: https://www.ismp.org/orderforms/reporterrortoismp.asp.

2. The *FDA MedWatch* program tracks information on serious adverse drug events, potential and actual product use errors, and product quality problems.

   Technicians can access the FDA MedWatch program at: https://www.accessdata.fda.gov/scripts/medwatch/medwatch-online.htm.

3. The *USP MEDMARX Reporting System* is a subscription-based system used in many hospitals. The system allows internal documentation and data tracking on medication hazards, errors, and adverse events.

4. Agency for Healthcare Research and Quality (AHRQ).

5. American Society of Health-System Pharmacists.

6. The Joint Commission (TJC).

V. Chapter Summary

A. Medication errors can occur because of individual or system-based causes. Pharmacy technicians should learn common causes and prevention strategies for medication errors.

B. If an error occurs, pharmacy technicians should follow pharmacy policy procedures regarding error documentation and reporting.

C. Technicians should report medication errors externally to national organizations that provide data to regulatory agencies and manufacturers to promote changes and improve patient safety.

VI. Questions for Discussion

A. What is the ISMP? What is this organization's role in error prevention?

B. How does tall-man lettering decrease medication errors?

C. Discuss types of medication errors that can occur in electronic prescribing systems.

D. List examples of error prone abbreviations commonly seen in practice.

VII. Sample Questions

1. A medication that has a high risk of injury if used inappropriately is a:

    a. dangerous medication
    b. high-alert medication
    c. warning medication
    d. red label medication

2. Adverse events are most often reported externally to which of the following systems?

    a. USP MEDMARX registry
    b. TJC Error System
    c. FDA MedWatch Program
    d. AHRQ Medication Error Reporting System

3. Which of these numeric doses is written with a "trailing" zero?

    a. 10 mg
    b. 0.1 mg
    c. 10.0 mg
    d. 100 mg

4. Which of the following choices is one of the five "rights" of safe medication use?

    a. right hospital
    b. right computer
    c. right prescription
    d. right dose

5. Which of the following is a subscription-based medication error documentation system used in many hospitals?

   a. USP MEDMARX Reporting System
   b. FDA MedWatch System
   c. ISMP Medication Errors Reporting Program
   d. AHRQ Error Reporting System

The **Answer Key** appears in **Section VIII**.

Notes:

Chapter 12

Pharmacy Quality Assurance

I. Key Terms and Concepts

A. *Quality assurance* refers to all factors that influence the quality of medication and related products, pharmacy services, and patient care in the medication use process.

B. *Quality improvement* is achieved by defining specific outcomes that are measured and monitored over time as changes are made in the system.

C. *Continuous quality improvement* is the philosophy of continually improving the processes associated with providing any good or service.

D. A *quality indicator* measures a particular process or outcome.

II. Quality Assurance in Pharmacy Practice

A. *Quality assurance* refers to all factors that influence the quality of medication and related products, pharmacy services, and patient care in the medication use process.

B. *Quality improvement* is achieved by defining specific outcomes that are measured and monitored for improvement over time as changes are made in the system.

C. *Continuous quality improvement* is the philosophy of continually improving the processes associated with providing any good or service.

D. A *quality indicator* measures a particular process or outcome. For example, when implementing a new patient safety initiative, the number of medication errors may be tracked.

E. Organizations such as *The Joint Commission* and the *Center for Pharmacy Practice Accreditation* accredit pharmacies in an effort to continually improve the quality of pharmacy care.

F. The pharmacy technician's role in quality assurance will usually encompass areas related to providing drug products and related services. Examples include quality processes in medication preparation and distribution, inventory control, productivity, efficiency, and communication.

III. Medication Error Prevention

A. As discussed in **Chapter 11**, implementing quality assurance and improvement processes in dispensing and distributing medication can help decrease medication errors. Examples of these measures include:

1. Asking another technician to double-check calculations for compounds.

2. Comparing computer-generated labels or printed prescription records with hard copies of prescriptions or medication orders to verify the accuracy of order entry.

3. Checking that the National Drug Code (NDC) numbers match on the stock bottle and computer-generated pharmacy label.

4. Posting lists of look-alike, sound-alike drugs in the pharmacy.

5. Verifying allergies, address, and date of birth with individuals on prescription drop off or pick up.

6. Participating in regularly occurring staff discussions of medication errors or "near-misses" in the pharmacy to prevent future errors. This quality improvement strategy is required by some state boards of pharmacy.

IV. Deterring Drug Theft and/or Diversion

A. *Drug theft* and *drug diversion* are terms for illegally obtaining any medication. The drugs usually affected are controlled substances.

B. Pharmacy quality policies to deter theft often include:

1. Storing controlled substances in a locked cabinet.

2. Periodically conducting a physical inventory of controlled substances and monitoring the inventory on an ongoing basis. **Chapter 13** contains more information on inventory management.

3. Maintaining records on controlled substances. **Chapter 3** contains additional information on laws related to controlled substances.

4. Allowing only a licensed pharmacist to dispense medications after hours.

V. Productivity, Efficiency, and Customer Satisfaction Measures

A. Quality assurance measures may include tracking customer wait times, improving efficiency in prescription or medication order processing, using customer satisfaction surveys, and analyzing communication practices within the pharmacy. The goal of quality assurance in this area is to improve pharmacy and staff productivity and efficiency and optimize patient or customer satisfaction. In the case of health-system pharmacy technicians, the pharmacy's "customers" may include other departments with which pharmacy directly interacts, such as nursing or medicine teams.

VI. Monitoring Policies and Procedures for Environmental Safety

A. Implementing quality processes related to environmental safety helps to ensure compliance with legal and regulatory standards and prevent exposure to hazardous substances. As detailed in **Chapter 13**, these areas include:

1. Sanitation management
2. Hazardous waste handling (e.g., needles)
3. Infection control (e.g., wearing protective clothing)

VII. Monitoring Routine Sanitation, Maintenance, and Calibration of Equipment

A. Quality processes ensure equipment is clean, well-maintained, calibrated, and functioning optimally for compounding and other pharmacy procedures. Specifically, pharmacies must:

1. Clean, sanitize, maintain, and calibrate equipment at regularly scheduled intervals (or more often as necessary) to prevent contamination and ensure proper performance.

2. Establish procedures for cleaning and maintaining equipment.

3. Keep records of equipment cleaning, maintenance, and inspection.

VIII. Inventory Control Systems

A. Quality processes in inventory control systems help to contain pharmacy costs and ensure accurate inventory records. As outlined in **Chapter 13**, examples of these processes include:

1. Routinely checking received items against invoices or packing slips when orders arrive in the pharmacy.

2. Comparing expiration dates of products received against those in stock to ensure that stock gets rotated and expired products are removed.

3. Using colored stickers to identify products that will expire soon.

4. Verifying that NDC numbers and bar codes of ordered items match the items received.

5. Double-counting quantities of controlled substance prescriptions.

IX. Communicating Changes in Product Availability

A. Products may become unavailable for several reasons, including recalls, formulary changes, discontinued products, or manufacturer shortages. Maintaining an efficient and effective system for communicating changes in product availability is an important element of a quality patient care system.

B. Methods for communicating product changes include:

1. Personal communication

   a. Communicating with the patient or patient's representative

   b. Staff meetings

2. Written communication

   a. Memorandum to staff and other health care professionals

   b. Pharmacy newsletter

   c. Institutional newsletter

X. Collecting and Analyzing Quality Data

A. Routine monitoring of the pharmacy department's activities helps ensure the quality of pharmacy products and services, and serves to identify existing and potential problems. Monitoring and measuring a specific outcome or *quality indicator* is part of the continuous quality improvement process.

B. Examples of quality indicators used to monitor pharmacy quality improvement include:

1. Sterile product testing
   a. Evaluating processes used in the preparation and sterilization of products to ensure that sterile products are free from microbial contamination, particulate matter, and pyrogens. This assessment includes various tests.
2. Packaging unit-dose medications
   a. Evaluating accuracy and efficiency in the packaging process
3. Medication errors
   a. Tracking the number of errors over a period of time
4. Drug distribution activities
   a. Evaluating accuracy in filling and checking unit-dose medication carts
5. Recordkeeping activities
   a. Evaluating or reviewing patient profiles, medication administration records, and other records related to the above processes
6. Inventory control
   a. Evaluating changes in inventory costs

XI. Chapter Summary

A. The pharmacy technician assists in pharmacy quality assurance procedures. Many pharmacy accrediting agencies require pharmacies to document their quality improvement processes. Quality assurance processes often include ongoing data collection and continual monitoring to reduce medication errors, deter theft, and improve pharmacy and staff productivity and efficiency, customer satisfaction with pharmacy services, environmental safety procedures, sanitation and maintenance of pharmacy equipment, inventory control measures, and strategies for communicating with patients and other health care providers.

B. Quality improvement measures include many best practices in dispensing, inventory control, compounding, and patient care. The pharmacy technician should learn pharmacy policies and procedures regarding quality assurance and improvement methods.

XII. Questions for Discussion

A. What are the differences between quality assurance and quality improvement?

B. Which quality improvement processes are most important? Why?

C. Discuss the quality improvement processes that contribute to medication safety.

D. How can quality improvement steps impact pharmacy costs and inventory control?

E. What is a quality indicator? How is it used in the quality improvement process?

XIII. Sample Questions

1. Which of the following is a philosophy of continually improving the process associated with providing any good or service?

   a. quality working
   b. continuous quality improvement
   c. perpetual inventory improvement
   d. quality indication

2. Which of the following provides an example of a quality improvement process to decrease medication errors?

   a. Asking another technician to double-check calculations for compounds
   b. Maintaining records of controlled substances
   c. Storing controlled substances in a locked cabinet
   d. Distributing a customer satisfaction survey

3. Which of the following contributes to pharmacy quality?

   a. Pharmacy accreditation
   b. Use of continuous quality improvement processes
   c. Monitoring quality indicators for areas of quality improvement
   d. All of the above

4. Which of the following provides an example of a quality improvement process for inventory control?

   a. Distributing a customer satisfaction survey
   b. Verifying patient allergy information on prescription drop off
   c. Verifying that the NDC numbers of ordered items match the received items
   d. Participating in discussions of "near misses" with pharmacy staff

The **Answer Key** appears in **Section VIII**.

Notes:

Section VI

Pharmacy Inventory Management

Kristin W. Weitzel

Section VI outlines the knowledge and activities required for inventory control, drug storage, inventory return, and hazardous product disposal, including:

- processes and terminology for ordering inventory
- requirements for receiving and storing inventory
- rules governing removal and disposal of hazardous waste and other drug products
- strategies for processing returns for unused or expired products

Chapter 13

Inventory Management, Storage, Returns, and Disposal

I. Key Terms and Concepts

A. *Pharmacy inventory* includes any product or merchandise (e.g., drugs, devices) available to meet future demand.

B. The manufacturer's *expiration date* indicates the date until which the manufacturer can guarantee the full potency and safety of the drug, provided it is stored under required conditions.

C. *Inventory turnover rate* refers to the number of times a product is purchased, sold, and replaced during a specific accounting period.

D. *Par level* denotes the inventory level at which a drug is automatically reordered.

E. *Reverse distributors* assist in returning expired or unusable products to help maintain compliance with the manufacturer's return policies. They also receive and process return credits.

F. A pharmaceutical *waste stream* describes the specific type of waste generated by a pharmacy and how the waste gets disposed.

G. The *Material Safety Data Sheet (MSDS)* gives information on the storage, handling, and disposal of hazardous drugs products, such as chemotherapy agents.

II. Identifying Drug Products for Inventory and Tracking

A. The *National Drug Code* (NDC) *number* is a unique 3-segment, 10-digit identification number assigned to each medication. Each human drug must have an NDC number as a unique product identification number.

NDCs follow one of the following numeric sequence configurations to make up the total 10 digits: 4-4-2, 5-3-2, or 5-4-1. For example, the NDC number for a 30-count bottle of Lexapro 10 mg tablets labeled by Physician's Total Care, Inc., is 54868-4700-1, which follows the 5-4-1 numeric sequence configuration.

The first segment, or the *labeler code*, is assigned by the Food and Drug Administration (FDA) and identifies the labeler (manufacturer, repackager, or distributor).

The second segment, or the *product code*, is assigned by the labeler and identifies the drug product, including its strength and dosage form for the specific manufacturer.

The third segment, or the *package code,* is also assigned by the labeler and identifies package size and type.

In the Lexapro 10 mg example (NDC = 54868-4700-1), the numeric segments provide the following information:

54868	Labeler code; indicates Physician's Total Care, Inc.
4700	Product code; indicates product is Lexapro 10 mg tablets.
1	Package code; indicates package type and size is a bottle of 30.

When pulling drugs from the shelf, technicians must verify that the intended and actual NDC numbers match. A mismatched NDC could indicate that the wrong drug, formulation, strength, or package size is being ordered or dispensed.

B. Manufacturers use *lot numbers* to identify internal production batches of drugs and other products. Lot numbers help trace specific products that require recall or removal from inventory.

C. The manufacturer's *expiration date*, or shelf life, must appear on drugs and other pharmacy products. The expiration date indicates the date until which the manufacturer can guarantee the full potency and safety of the drug, provided that it is stored under required conditions.

Technicians should never dispense drug products after their expiration date. Inventory systems must include a process for detecting and returning expired or "short-dated" medications and products (products very close to the manufacturer's expiration date).

D. The *beyond-use date* indicates the date after which the prepared or dispensed prescription may not be used by the patient. Technicians must clearly differentiate this date from the manufacturer's expiration date.

As detailed in **Section IV**, the beyond-use date for compounded prescriptions is set at the time of preparation. For nonsterile medications repackaged from the manufacturer's stock bottles into multi-dose or unit-dose containers, many state Boards of Pharmacy require that the beyond-use date be set at one year from the original dispensing date. The beyond-use date should never exceed the manufacturer's expiration date.

III. Inventory Terminology

A. The term *inventory* refers to pharmacy products or merchandise (e.g., drugs, devices) available to meet future demand.

B. *Inventory management* is the system of ordering, storing, repackaging, and disposing of pharmacy products and merchandise. Pharmacies must have an inventory management system to ensure that:

1. Needed drugs remain available to fill prescriptions;
2. Unexpected drug shortages remain minimally disruptive to patient care;
3. Products get purchased at the best price; and
4. Drugs are ordered and disposed of efficiently.

C. Pharmacies use specific *inventory control* procedures to purchase products in sufficient quantity to meet the anticipated demands of customers, while controlling inventory size and costs. **Chapter 19** contains additional information on inventory control.

D. *Inventory turnover rate* refers to the number of times pharmacies purchase, sell, and replace a product during a specific accounting period.

E. *Par level* denotes the inventory level at which a drug is automatically reordered. For example, when one stock bottle of amoxicillin 500 mg capsules remains on the shelf, pharmacies may automatically reorder the drug.

F. *Stock rotation* involves managing inventory costs by first using drug products that will expire soonest. For example, if two bottles of sertraline 50 mg remain on the pharmacy shelf, try to dispense the one that will expire first. This will help minimize the risk of a product expiring and then needing to be returned to the wholesaler for a partial credit.

G. Some pharmacies use *automated order systems* along with their inventory systems. Automated order systems reconcile actual drug inventory levels in the pharmacy computer when a drug gets dispensed, using bar code or other technology. When a drug quantity reaches a predetermined par level, that drug is automatically added to a daily order list or ordered electronically.

IV. Ordering Inventory

A. Identifying products that require ordering

1. Determining which products to order depends on the inventory purchasing procedures of each individual pharmacy. Factors that influence product ordering decisions include expected inventory turnover rate, manufacturing sources, and purchase price.

2. The *formulary* or preferred drug list will also influence ordering decisions, because medications included in the institution's formulary or those medications preferred by payers will be dispensed more frequently. **Chapter 7** contains additional information on formulary and preferred drug lists.

B. Depending on the pharmacy's ordering system, technicians may need to enter the following information when ordering products:

1. Pharmaceuticals

    a. Drug name and manufacturer

    b. Strength and dosage form of the medication (e.g., tablets, capsules, solutions, suspensions, injections, suppositories)

    c. Type of packaging (unit-dose or bulk packaging)

    d. Quantity contained in the unit desired (e.g., 100's, 16 oz.)

    e. Number of units

2. Equipment, devices, and supplies

    a. Name and manufacturer of product

    b. Strength or size (if applicable) of product

    c. Quantity contained in the unit desired

    d. Number of units

    e. Other information as required

C. Each pharmacy's ordering policies will determine the product sources. Technicians should familiarize themselves with the ordering practices within their pharmacy. Drugs may be ordered and received from:

1. Wholesale drug distributors

2. Manufacturers
3. Other pharmacies

D. Controlled substances

Ordering procedures for controlled substances may require additional documentation. Controlled substances are classified as Schedules I through V, with the most frequently encountered controlled substances falling in Schedules II, III, and IV. Schedule II drugs such as oxycodone or methadone have a higher abuse potential and are subject to stricter documentation requirements than Schedule III or IV medications (e.g., hydrocodone combination products, alprazolam). **Chapter 3** outlines the recordkeeping requirements of controlled substances.

E. Investigational drugs

Physicians conduct investigational drug studies in various practice settings to gather information about the appropriate use, efficacy, dosage, and safety of drugs that look promising for treating particular diseases. **Chapter 3** contains more information on recordkeeping procedures for investigational drugs.

F. Expediting emergency orders

1. Technicians should understand the delivery timetables of goods ordered from various sources. In the event that the pharmacy needs drugs quickly, technicians can obtain them from the most desirable source in accordance with pharmacy policies and procedures.

2. In an emergency, the usual preferred sources may not be feasible, and the pharmacy may need to borrow or purchase the product from a nearby pharmacy or institution.

V. Receiving Inventory

A. Verifying specifications on original purchase orders

1. Verifying products ordered versus products received. To ensure that the correct product was sent by the manufacturer or wholesale distributor, the technician must carefully examine the order and confirm that the information is consistent in all the components. Technicians should verify consistency with the original purchase order or “want book,” the invoice or packing slip received with the order, and the products received in the order.

   The following information should be compared and verified in each of the following components for appropriateness and accuracy:

   a. Drug name and manufacturer

   b. Strength and dosage form of medication

   c. Appropriateness of packaging type (e.g., unit-dose versus bulk packaging)

d. Quantity contained in the unit desired (e.g., 100's, 16 oz.)

e. Number of units received versus number ordered

2. Documenting goods received

a. Pharmaceuticals, durable medical equipment, devices, and supplies

(1) Technicians should note on the invoice the products received, as well as any product shortages.

b. Controlled substances

(1) Controlled substances require additional documentation. **Chapter 3** details the recordkeeping requirements for controlled substances.

c. Investigational drugs

(1) Investigational drugs require additional documentation. **Chapter 3** outlines the recordkeeping requirements for investigational drugs.

VI. Storing Inventory

A. Technicians should learn which products require special storage conditions (e.g., refrigeration) and place products into inventory under proper storage conditions.

Specific temperature requirements exist for prescribed storage conditions. Technicians must follow these requirements and document temperatures closely in accordance with state- or practice-specific requirements, the drug product, and other factors. Technicians should familiarize themselves with drug storage and temperature monitoring requirements in their practice setting.

Definitions for common drug storage temperature requirements include:

1. Room temperature – temperature between 20° and 25°C (68° and 77°F)
2. Refrigeration – temperature between 2° and 8°C (36° and 46°F)
3. Freezing – temperature between –25° and –10°C (–13° and 14°F)

Chapter 16 details temperature conversion formulas.

B. Technicians must place products into inventory according to stock rotation procedures. Place items that will expire soonest in front of items with longer expiration dates.

C. Technicians should store all Schedule II medications in a locked area in the pharmacy.

D. Controlled substances require additional steps for monitoring ongoing inventory levels. Federal and state law require that pharmacies conduct a *biennial inventory* (every 2 years) of all controlled substances, including an exact count of Schedule II medications and an approximate count of Schedule III, IV, and V drugs. A *perpetual inventory* of Schedule II medications shows all drugs received or dispensed at any time and gives the actual quantity of any Schedule II medication on hand. Some states require an ongoing perpetual inventory count of Schedule II drugs.

E. The *MSDS* provides information on the storage and handling of hazardous drug products, such as chemotherapy agents. Technicians should use the MSDS as a guide for storing hazardous drugs, in addition to any institution policies and procedures.

VII. Repackaging Medications

A. Repackaging finished dosage forms for dispensing (e.g., unit-dose packaging)

1. Most drugs may be ordered in unit-dose packaging, but technicians may need to repackage them when commercially available products need to fit into automated dispensing machines, specialized drug-delivery systems, or unit-dose delivery systems (e.g., blister cards). Technicians should familiarize themselves with the pharmacy's policies and procedures for repackaging.

2. Documenting repackaged items may require entering the following information into the inventory records:

    a. Date the drug was removed from bulk inventory into repackaged form

    b. Drug name, strength, dosage form, and quantity used

    c. Lot number

    d. Initials of technician and supervising pharmacist

    e. Other information as required by pharmacy policies

VIII. Removing Medications and Other Products from Inventory

A. Pharmacies have policies and procedures to prospectively identify and remove expired, discontinued, and slow-moving products from inventory on a regular basis. Store expired and other products removed from pharmacy inventory separately from remaining normal inventory.

B. Technicians should know procedures for responding to product withdrawals and FDA recalls of drugs, equipment, devices, or supplies. This includes removing products from inventory and notifying patients and prescribers as needed, in accordance with pharmacy policies and procedures. In the event of an FDA recall, the required steps will depend on the recall type. FDA recalls are classified as:

1. Class I – reasonable probability that use or exposure will cause serious consequences or death.

2. Class II – use or exposure may cause temporary or reversible adverse consequences, with a remote probability of serious consequences.

3. Class III – use or exposure is not likely to cause adverse consequences.

C. Additional rules and regulations apply to removing controlled substances from inventory. **Chapter 3** contains additional information on regulations pertaining to controlled substances.

D. **Chapter 3** outlines additional steps required for removing investigational drugs from inventory.

IX. Returning or Disposing of Inventory

A. In most cases, pharmacies return expired, discontinued, recalled, or otherwise unusable products to the seller. Some vendors, wholesalers, or manufacturers accept outdated or expired products for a partial credit on return. Technicians should learn the policies and procedures for returning outdated, discontinued, or recalled drug products.

B. Many pharmacies utilize *reverse distributors* to return outdated or recalled medications to the manufacturer. Reverse distributors help pharmacies maintain compliance with manufacturer's return policies and assist with receiving and processing return credits.

C. Some medications (e.g., partial vials used in preparing compounded products) cannot be returned. Technicians should learn pharmacy policies and procedures for disposing of or destroying pharmacy products that cannot be returned.

D. Pharmacies need to manage the environmental impact of pharmaceutical waste in accordance with federal and state laws and regulations. A *waste stream* describes the specific type of waste generated by a pharmacy and disposal procedures. For example, chemotherapy or cytotoxic medications should be destroyed in the appropriate hazardous waste stream.

E. The MSDS provides guidance on disposal information and personal protection for hazardous drug spills or waste.

F. Technicians should always use sharps containers to dispose of used needles, syringes, ampules, and vials used in pharmacies.

G. Pharmacies should use biohazard containers or receptacles for disposing of any clothing that comes in contact with body fluid or hazardous substances, such as gloves, gowns, and masks.

H. Return or disposal of controlled substances requires additional documentation depending on the specific drug and the pharmacy's policies and procedures. **Chapter 3** details these recordkeeping requirements. Controlled substances can be returned only by facilities that have a Drug Enforcement Administration (DEA) number.

I. Return or disposal of unused investigational drugs requires different procedures.

X. Chapter Summary

A. As one of their primary responsibilities, pharmacy technicians will need to monitor medication distribution and inventory control systems.

B. Technicians should learn the pharmacy's policies and procedures related to ordering products, receiving goods, storing, returning, and disposing of products in inventory.

XI. Questions for Discussion

A. What factors should technicians consider in determining which products to order for the pharmacy?

B. What factors should technicians consider in determining what quantity of a particular product to order?

C. What factors should technicians consider in identifying the appropriate supplier for ordering a particular product?

D. Why do different classifications of product recalls exist? What is the potential response to each type of recall?

E. Discuss the impact that pharmaceutical waste can have on the environment. What steps can technicians take to minimize this impact?

XII. Sample Questions

1. The second segment of the NDC number identifies:

    a. the manufacturer
    b. the drug product
    c. the package size
    d. the package type

2. Until which date can the manufacturer guarantee the full potency and safety of a drug, as long as it is stored according to manufacturer's instructions?

    a. expiration date
    b. beyond-use date
    c. NDC date
    d. compounding date

3. Which of the following pharmacy organizations provides guidance on defining and setting expiration and beyond-use dating for the pharmacy profession?

   a. FDA
   b. DEA
   c. CMS
   d. USP

4. The number of times a product is purchased, sold, and replaced during a specific accounting period is called the:

   a. inventory control period
   b. inventory turnover rate
   c. inventory management rate
   d. inventory level

5. When the pharmacy receives orders, the technician should verify that the order components agree with the:

   a. original purchase order
   b. invoice or packing slip
   c. products received in the order
   d. all of the above

6. If a drug requires storage at room temperature, which of the following temperature ranges would be acceptable?

   a. 52° to 66°F
   b. 64° to 70°F
   c. 68° to 77°F
   d. 78° to 87°F

7. The required inventory of controlled substances that takes place every two years is called:

   a. annual inventory
   b. biennial inventory
   c. required inventory
   d. pharmacy inventory

8. Which of the following provides storage and disposal information for hazardous drug substances?

   a. Hazardous Data Information Sheet
   b. Disposal and Storage Sheet
   c. Material Safety Data Sheet
   d. Material Storage Disposal Sheet

9. If a drug is the subject of an FDA Class I recall, what probability exists of serious consequences or death?

   a. reasonable probability
   b. low probability
   c. no probability
   d. not enough information is provided

10. A pharmaceutical waste stream:

   a. is required by the DEA
   b. describes how the pharmacy disposes of a specific type of waste
   c. is needed only in community pharmacies
   d. is optional for all pharmacy settings

The **Answer Key** appears **in Section VIII.**

Notes:

Section VII

Pharmaceutical Calculations

William A. Hopkins Jr.

Section VII outlines mathematical calculations related to the pharmacy practice site, such as:

- calculating doses and injection flow rates
- converting between units of measurement
- preparing percentages
- reducing and enlarging formulas
- determining charges for prescriptions and medication orders

Chapter 14

Fractions, Decimals, and Roman Numerals

I. Fractions

A. Components of fractions

1. Example: 5/8

Numerator	5
Fraction line	—
Denominator	8

B. Types of common fractions

1. Proper fractions

a. Proper fractions have a smaller numerator than denominator.

(1) Example: 5/8

2. Improper fractions

a. Improper fractions have a larger numerator than denominator.

(1) Example: 8/5

b. Reduce improper fractions to mixed numbers.

(1) Example: 8/5 should be reduced to 1 3/5

3. Simple fractions

a. Simple fractions are proper fractions reduced to lowest terms.

(1) Example: 15/24 = 5/8

4. Complex fractions

   a. Complex fractions are "fractions of fractions," where both the numerator and denominator are fractions.

      (1) Example: $\frac{5/8}{1/2}$

C. Reducing fractions to lowest terms

1. To reduce a fraction to lowest terms, divide both the numerator and denominator by the largest multiple common to both terms. The fraction will maintain its value but change its form.

   a. Example: 15/24 is reduced to 5/8 by dividing both numerator and denominator by 3:

$$\frac{15 \div 3}{24 \div 3} = \frac{5}{8}$$

D. Five rules for calculating with fractions

1. Understand the impact of multiplying or dividing the numerator and/or denominator by a whole number.

   Example: 4/8

$$\frac{4 \times 2}{8} = \frac{8}{8} = 1 \qquad \frac{4}{8 \times 2} = \frac{4}{16} = \frac{1}{4}$$

$$\frac{4 \div 2}{8} = \frac{2}{8} = \frac{1}{4} \qquad \frac{4}{8 \div 2} = \frac{4}{4} = 1$$

2. Convert mixed numbers or whole numbers to improper fractions before performing calculations with other fractions.

   a. Example: 2 7/8 = 23/8

3. When adding or subtracting fractions, make sure all fractions have a common denominator (i.e., a number into which all denominators may be divided an even number of times).

   a. Example: 3/4, 5/8, 1/2 may be written as 6/8, 5/8, 4/8

4. Convert answers that are improper fractions back to whole numbers or mixed numbers.

   a. Example: 15/3 = 5

5. Convert answers to lowest terms

   a. Example: 16/32 = 8/16 = 4/8 = 2/4 = 1/2

E. Adding and subtracting fractions

1. First convert all fractions to a common denominator. Then add or subtract the numerators.

   a. Example: 1/2 + 5/6 + 3/8 = 12/24 + 20/24 + 9/24 = 41/24 = 1 17/24

   b. Example: 13/32 – 3/8 = 13/32 – 12/32 = 1/32

F. Multiplying fractions

1. Unlike addition and subtraction, multiplying fractions does not require common denominators. Multiply numerators by numerators and denominators by denominators.

   a. Example: 9 2/7 × 3/4 = 65/7 × 3/4 = 195/28 = 6 27/28

G. Dividing fractions

1. Invert the divisor and multiply the fractions.

   a. Example: 11/12 ÷ 1/6 = 11/12 × 6/1 = 66/12 = 5 1/2

   b. Example: 10 3/5 ÷ 2 1/10 = 53/5 ÷ 21/10 = 53/5 × 10/21 = 530/105 = 5 5/105 = 5 1/21

II. Decimals

A. Converting decimals to fractions

1. Decimal fractions are fractions with denominators of 10 and/or multiples of 10.

   a. A decimal number with one digit to the right of the decimal point is expressed in "tenths."

      (1) Example: 0.7 = 7/10

   b. A decimal number with two digits to the right of the decimal point is expressed as "hundredths."

      (1) Example: 0.27 = 27/100

   c. Follow the same rule as more digits are added to the right of the decimal point.

      (1) Example: 0.0365 = 365/10,000

B. Converting fractions to decimals

1. To convert common fractions to decimal fractions, divide the numerator by the denominator.

    a. Example: 3/4 = 0.75

    b. Example: 1 5/8 = 13/8 = 1.625

C. Adding, subtracting, multiplying, and dividing decimals

1. When adding, subtracting, multiplying, and dividing decimals and common fractions, convert all terms to the same system before performing the calculation.

    a. Example: 25/100 + 1.005 = 0.25 + 1.005 = 1.255

III. Roman Numerals

A. Primary Roman numeral units

SS = 1/2
I or i = 1
V = 5
X = 10
L = 50
C = 100
D = 500
M = 1000

B. Eight rules for using Roman numerals

1. When a numeral is repeated, its value is repeated.

    a. Example: XX = 10 + 10 = 20

2. A numeral may not be repeated more than three times.

    a. Example: XL = 40 (not XXXX)

3. V, L, and D are never repeated. VV is incorrect.

4. When a smaller numeral is placed before a larger numeral, it is subtracted from the larger numeral.

    a. Example: XC = 100 – 10 = 90

5. When a smaller numeral is placed after a larger numeral, it is added to the larger numeral.

    a. Example: CX = 100 + 10 = 110

6. V, L, and D are never subtracted. VX is incorrect.

7. Never subtract more than one numeral.

    a. Example: VIII = 8 (not IIX)

8. Only subtract I, X, and C from the next two highest numerals, as follows:

    a. Only subtract I from V and X.
    b. Only subtract X from L and C.
    c. Only subtract C from D and M.

IV. Sample Questions

1. Reduce the following fractions to lowest terms:

    a. 10/75 = _____
    b. 8/16 = _____
    c. 3/15 = _____
    d. 60/186 = _____

2. Convert the following numbers to improper fractions:

    a. 5 = _____
    b. 3 2/3 = _____

3. Convert the following groups of fractions into groups of fractions with common denominators:

    a. 15/32, 3/16, 7/64 = _____, _____, _____
    b. 3/4, 7/8, 5/12 = _____, _____, _____

4. Convert 15/4 into a whole or mixed number: 15/4 = _____

5. 3/4 + 1 1/8 = _____

6. 7 5/8 – 1 1/3 = _____

7. 1 3/4 × 3 = _____

8. 1/2 ÷ 5 = _____

9. 3/16 ÷ 1 1/2 = _____

10. Convert the following decimal numbers to fractions:

    a. 0.07 = _____
    b. 0.077 = _____
    c. 5.0125 = _____

11. Convert the following fractions to decimal numbers:

    a. 3/8 = _____
    b. 2 7/13 = _____

12. Perform the following calculations:

    a. 3.75 – 1/2 = _____
    b. 3/4 × 2.5 = _____
    c. 2 3/8 ÷ 0.5 = _____

13. Express the following numbers as Roman numerals:

    a. 29 = _____
    b. 47 = _____
    c. 86 = _____
    d. 1154 = _____

14. Express the following Roman numerals as Arabic numerals:

    a. LXXVIII = _____
    b. CXIII = _____
    c. XCIV = _____
    d. MCMLXI = _____

15. How many 0.0125 grain (gr.) doses can be made from 3/8 gr. of a drug?

16. How many ounces of boric acid would be left in an 8-oz. bottle if you dispensed 2 prescriptions each containing 1 1/4 oz. of boric acid and 3 additional prescriptions each containing 1.75 oz. from the bottle?

17. How many 1/40 gr. tablets would provide 1/200 gr. of a drug?

18. How many 1/400 gr. nitroglycerin tablets would provide 1/150 gr. of nitroglycerin?

19. If 10 patients each receive XLIV mg of a drug, how many total milligrams (in Roman numerals) would all the patients receive?

20. How much would a compounded ointment weigh if it contained the following weights of various drugs and vehicles: IX grams, VI grams, and LX grams?

21. How many pounds of a chemical remain if a manufacturer has DXV pounds of the chemical and uses LXVI pounds to manufacture a bulk powder?

22. A capsule contains CDXLV milligrams of a drug. How many milligrams would be in 20 capsules?

23. Express the total weight in Roman numerals of 4 applications of an eye ointment if each application weighs 251 mg.

24. How many prescriptions (in Roman numerals) are filled in a pharmacy over 4 days if the pharmacy averages CXX prescriptions daily?

25. a. How many pounds of sulfur powder does a pharmacy have on hand if the pharmacy has 3 containers each containing 3/8 lb. of sulfur?

    b. How much sulfur would remain if you gave 3/16 lb. of sulfur to another pharmacy?

26. A hospitalized patient received 4 doses of 1/150 gr. nitroglycerin tablets in 1 day. How many grains of nitroglycerin did the patient receive? *(Express answer as a decimal fraction.)*

27. a. A 120-mL bottle of children's antihistamine syrup contains 24 tsp. doses. How many milliliters must be in a dose?

    b. How many doses would be in the bottle if a young child receives 3/4 tsp. of the syrup per dose?

28. How many milligrams of aspirin would be in XXIV tablets if each tablet contains 325 mg of aspirin?

29. a. A pharmacy technician has 200 g of Drug B on hand. How much will be required to fill 100 capsules each containing 1 1/8 g of Drug B?

    b. How many grams of Drug B remain after filling the capsules?

30. If the average pharmacy technician can prepare CIX prescriptions daily, how many technicians would be required to prepare MDCXXXV prescriptions?

31. How many 0.004 g doses can be made from 3/4 g of a drug?

The **Answer Key** appears in **Section VIII**.

Notes:

Chapter 15

Calculating Percentage and Ratio Strength

I. Percentage

A. Percent and its corresponding sign (%) mean "parts in one hundred."

1. Example: 40% may be expressed as:

   a. 40 parts in 100

   b. 40/100

   c. 0.40

   d. 2/5 (40/100 = 4/10 = 2/5)

B. Converting percents to decimals

1. To convert a percent to a decimal, remove the percent sign and move the decimal point two places to the left.

   a. Examples: 58% = 0.58 72% = 0.72

C. Converting decimals to percents

1. To convert a decimal to a percent, move the decimal point two places to the right and add the percent sign.

   a. Example: 0.17 = 17%

D. Converting fractions to percents

1. To convert a fraction to a percent, reduce the fraction to a decimal, then move the decimal point two places to the right, and add the percent sign.

   a. Example: 1/2 = 0.50 = 50%

E. Expressing a percent as a ratio

1. A ratio is the relationship or comparison of two like quantities.

    a. Example: 1/2 expressed as a ratio would be 1:2 or "one part in two parts."
    This can also be expressed as:

    (1) a decimal (0.5)

    (2) a percent (50%)

II. Ratio and Proportion

A. Proportion

1. A proportion expresses the equality of two ratios or fractions. Most pharmacy calculations can be performed using the principles of ratio and proportion.

B. Basic algebraic expression

1. The simplest algebraic form for a ratio and proportion is: A/B = C/D, or A:B = C:D

C. Solving for an unknown

1. By setting two equal ratios together, you may easily solve for an unknown if you know three of the four terms of the proportion.

    a. Example: 3/5 = x/15
    This can be restated as, "if there are 3 parts in 5 parts, then there are x parts in 15 parts."
    Cross multiply to get: 5(x) = 45
    Rearrange the equation to: (x) = 45/5
    Divide to get the solution: x = 45/5 = 9
    Therefore, 3/5 = 9/15, or "3 parts in 5 parts is equivalent to 9 parts in every 15 parts."

III. Sample Questions

1. Convert the following problems:

    a. 72% = 72/100 = 0.______

    b. 0.35 = 35% = ______/100 = 7/______

    c. 25% = 25/100 = ______:100

d. 0.182 = _____%

e. 3/8 = 0. _____ = _____%

2. Using the principles of ratio and proportion, solve the following problems:

   a. If 10 lb. of drug cost $200, what would 2 lb. cost?

   b. How many pounds could you buy for $25?

   c. What would 10 oz. cost (16 oz. per 1 lb.)?

3. A formula for 1000 tablets contains 11.5 g of an antihistamine. How many grams of the antihistamine should be used to prepare 475 tablets?

4. A cough syrup contains 5 mg of a drug in each 15 mL dose. How many milligrams of drug would be contained in a 480 mL bottle of syrup?

5. If 2 tablets contain 650 mg of acetaminophen, how many milligrams would be contained in a bottle of 100 tablets?

6. If 7 tablets contain 35 mg of diazepam, how many tablets would contain 1500 mg?

7. If a patient pays $0.58 per tablet for 90 tablets, how much does the entire prescription cost?

8. How many grams of codeine sulfate would be required to prepare 20 capsules, each containing 0.0325 g of codeine sulfate?

9. How much would 100 lb. of a chemical cost if 385 lb. cost $795?

10. How many kilograms would a 173-lb. patient weigh if there are 2.2 lb. in every kilogram?

11. If a penicillin solution contains 6 million units of penicillin in 10 mL, how many units would be contained in a 0.5 mL dose?

12. If a patient receives 5 mL of intravenous fluid per minute, how much fluid would the patient receive each hour?

13. How many milligrams of amoxicillin would a patient receive in 1 week if the patient receives 750 mg each day?

14. If a syringe contains 28 mg of drug in 3 mL, how many milligrams of the drug would a patient receive if 1.2 mL is administered?

15. If a 480 mL bottle of 10% potassium chloride solution contains 10 g of potassium chloride in every 100 mL of solution, how much potassium chloride will a patient receive from a 15 mL dose of the solution?

16. In the previous question, how much would the bottle of potassium chloride cost if the 15 mL dose cost $0.28?

17. a. If 12 prescription bottles cost $1.80, how much would 9 bottles cost?

    b. How much would a case containing 10 dozen bottles cost?

18. a. If a technician fills 1 prescription every 270 seconds, how many minutes would it take to fill a single prescription?

    b. How many prescriptions can the technician fill in a 7.5-hour workday?

19. a. A tablet contains 5 mg of an active ingredient. How many tablets should be dispensed for 1 month (*assume 30 days*) of therapy if the patient receives 1 tablet t.i.d.?

    b. How many milligrams of the drug will the patient receive in 1 month?

20. a. A 454 g jar of ointment contains 4.54 g of hydrocortisone. What is the decimal fraction of hydrocortisone in the ointment?

    b. What is the **percent strength** of this ointment?

21. A cream is labeled 20% strength. Express this value as a **ratio strength**.

22. a. If 6 oz. of a drug cost $88, how much would 1/4 oz. cost?

    b. How much of the drug can be purchased for $1?

23. a. If 100 capsules contain 3/8 g of an active ingredient, how many grams will 50 capsules contain? Express answer as a common fraction.

    b. Express the previous answer as a percent of a gram.

The **Answer Key** appears in **Section VIII**.

Notes:

Chapter 16

Pharmaceutical Systems of Measurement

I. Metric System

A. Primary units of measurement (subdivided by multiples of 10)

1. Length: meter (m)

2. Volume: liter (L or l)

3. Weight: gram (g)

B. Common prefixes

1. "Increasing" prefix

   a. "Kilo-" (1000) is the most common increasing prefix.

      (1) Example: 1 kilogram (kg) = 1000 g

2. "Decreasing" prefixes

   a. "Milli-" (1/1000)

      (1) Example: 1 milligram (mg) = 0.001 g (1/1000 g)

      (2) Example: 1 g = 1000 mg

   b. "Micro-" (1/1,000,000)

      (1) Example: 1 microgram (mcg) = 0.000001 g

      (2) Example: 1 g = 1,000,000 mcg

II. Common Conversions Between Systems

A. "Rounded-off" conversion factors

1. Weight

    a. 1 gram (g) = 15.4 grains (gr.)

    b. 1 grain (gr.) = 65 milligrams (mg)

    c. 1 pound (lb.) = 454 grams (g)

    d. 1 kilogram (kg) = 2.2 pounds (lb.)

    e. 1 ounce (oz.) = 28.4 grams (g)

    f. 1 ounce (oz.) = 437.5 grains (gr.)

    g. 1 pound (lb.) = 16 ounces (oz.)

2. Volume

    a. 1 fluid ounce = 30 milliliters (mL)

    b. 1 pint = 16 fluid ounces = 480 milliliters
    (*Note:* Sometimes the label on a pint bottle will read 473 mL instead of 480 mL. A fluid ounce actually contains 29.57 mL but is frequently rounded to 30 mL.)

    c. 1 gallon = 4 quarts = 8 pints = 128 fluid ounces = 3840 milliliters

3. Length

    a. 1 inch = 2.54 cm

III. Temperature Conversions

A. Converting degrees centigrade to degrees Fahrenheit

1. °F = 32 + 9/5 °C

    a. Example: 25°C
    32 + 9/5 (25) = 77°F

B. Converting degrees Fahrenheit to degrees centigrade

1. °C = 5/9 (°F – 32)

    a. Example: 32°F
    5/9 (32 – 32) = 0°C

IV. Sample Questions

1. Convert the following metric system units:

    a. 225 kilometers = ________m

    b. 525 g = ________kg

    c. 5 g = ________mg = ________mcg

    d. 350 mL = ________L

2. Calculate the following conversions:

    a. 16 fluid oz. = 1 pt. = ________mL

    b. 2 pt. = 1 qt. = ________fluid oz.

    c. 4 qt. = 1 gal. = ________pt. = ________fluid oz.

3. Solve the following conversions:

    a. 16 oz. = 1 lb. = ________gr.

    b. 3 inches = ________cm

4. Using the rounded-off conversion factor for weight, fill in the blanks:

    a. 1 gr. = ________g = ________mg

    b. 1 oz. = ________gr. = ________g

    c. 1 lb. = ________oz. = ________g = ________gr. = ________kg

    d. 1 kg = ________lb.

5. Using the rounded-off conversion factor for volume, fill in the blanks:

    a. 1 pt. = ________fluid oz. = ________mL

    b. 1 gal. = ________fluid oz. = ________mL = ________L

6. Convert 20°C to degrees Fahrenheit.

7. Convert 212°F to degrees centigrade.

8. How many 325 mg aspirin tablets can be prepared from 1/2 kg of aspirin?

9. How many kilograms would a 246-lb. patient weigh?

10. A 10 mL vial contains 40 mg of a drug. How many micrograms would be administered by injection of 2 mL of the drug?

11. If a physician orders 10 g of drug per liter, how many grains would be in 250 mL?

12. a. A pharmacy purchases 1.8 lb. of an antibiotic powder for compounding. How many ounces were purchased?

    b. How much did the bulk powder cost if 1 oz. costs $8.75?

    c. How much would 3/4 oz. cost?

13. a. How many 4 fluid oz. bottles can be filled from 3 gal. of syrup?

    b. How much would 1 bottle cost if the syrup sells for $40 per gallon?

14. a. How many kilograms of a drug would be needed to manufacture 800,000 tablets, each containing 15 mg of the drug?

    b. Express the previous answer in pounds.

    c. Express the previous answer in ounces.

    d. How much would the total amount of drug in the previous question cost if 1 oz. sells for $14.85?

15. a. A patient weighs 185 lb., but a drug is dosed on the basis of the patient's weight in kilograms. How many kilograms does the patient weigh?

    b. How much of a drug should this patient receive if the recommended dose is 3 mg/kg of body weight?

16. The temperature last January in Moscow was –58°F. Express this temperature in degrees centigrade.

17. A certain plastic cracks at –15°C. Express this temperature in degrees Fahrenheit.

The **Answer Key** appears in **Section VIII**.

Notes:

Chapter 17

Dosage Calculations

I. Basic Principles of Dosing

A. Definitions

1. Dose

a. The quantity of a drug taken by a patient is known as the dose. The dose may be expressed as a daily dose, single dose, or a total dose.

(1) A single dose is given once daily.

(2) A daily dose may be given once daily (as a single dose), or may be divided throughout the day.

(3) A total dose refers to the entire quantity of the drug taken throughout therapy.

2. Dosage regimen

a. A dosage regimen refers to the schedule of medication administration (e.g., every 4 hours, 3 times a day, at bedtime).

B. Doses vary tremendously because of differences in drug potency; routes of administration; the patient's age, weight, kidney and liver functions, etc. Many factors can enter into establishing a correct dose, and many dispensing errors are related to administering the wrong dose. Pharmacy technicians can contribute to patient care by learning appropriate doses of medications and by recalculating doses on questionable orders.

II. Manufacturer's Recommended Dose

A. Manufacturers of medications establish "normal doses" of their drugs through research. An established "normal dose" of a drug is known as the *manufacturer's recommended dose*.

B. Technicians can find information related to the manufacturer's recommended dose from numerous sources including package inserts, *Physician's Desk Reference*, *Facts and Comparisons*, and other sources.

C. Manufacturers usually list these recommended doses as milliliters or milligrams per kilogram (or pound) of body weight.

D. Technicians can usually perform the calculation of doses using the principles of ratio and proportion.

1. Example: The dose of a drug is 10 mg per kg of body weight. How much would you give a 220-lb. man?

    a. Step 1: 2.2 lb./1 kg = 220 lb./x
    x = 100 kg of body weight

    b. Step 2: 10 mg drug/1 kg = x/100 kg
    x = 1000 mg = 1 g of drug

III. Household Equivalents

A. Household equivalents are measurements frequently used in dosing. They are referred to as "household equivalents" because they are measures frequently found in homes (e.g., teaspoons, pints, tablespoons).

1. 1 teaspoonful (tsp., t) = 5 mL
2. 1 tablespoonful (tbsp., T) = 15 mL
3. 1 fluid ounce = 30 mL

IV. Flow Rate Calculations

A. Flow rate calculations are normally used for intravenous solutions and can be performed using "multiple" ratio and proportion calculations.

1. Example: If an intravenous order is for 500 mL of D5NS (5% dextrose in 0.9% sodium chloride) to be given over 4 hours (240 minutes), and the IV set delivers 15 drops (gtt.) per milliliter, what would be the flow rate in drops per minute?

Step 1: $$\frac{15 \text{ gtt.}}{1 \text{ mL}} = \frac{x}{500 \text{ mL}} \quad x = 7500 \text{ total drops (gtt.)}$$

Step 2: $$\frac{7500 \text{ gtt.}}{240 \text{ min.}} = \frac{x}{1 \text{ min.}} \quad x = 31 \text{ gtt./min.}$$

B. Another method for calculating flow rates is by using the following formula:

$$\frac{(\text{mL/hr.})\ (\text{gtt./mL})}{60\ \text{min./hr.}} = \text{flow rate in gtt./min.}$$

Using the above example:

$$\frac{(500\ \text{mL}/4\ \text{hr.})\ (15\ \text{gtt./mL})}{60\ \text{min./hr.}} = 31\ \text{gtt./min.}$$

V. Body Surface Area

A. Dosing by a patient's body surface area (BSA) is based on the individual's volume rather than weight. This method is used frequently with patients who are receiving chemotherapy and sometimes with children. BSA is measured in square meters (m^2), and most of the dosing will be in milligrams per square meter (mg/m^2).

1. BSA can be determined by finding out a patient's height and weight, and then using a nomogram, which is a graph with three columns of numbers: Height, Body Surface, and Mass (Weight). Once the patient's height and weight are marked, a line can be drawn between these two points using a straightedge. The point at which that line intersects the Body Surface column is the patient's BSA measurement.

   a. Five steps for determining a patient's BSA using a nomogram

      (1) Select the appropriate nomogram (i.e., adult or child).

      (2) Place a dot on the value for the patient's height (left vertical axis).

      (3) Place a dot on the value for the patient's weight (right vertical axis).

      (4) Connect the dots in steps 2 and 3 with a straightedge.

      (5) Read the patient's BSA located on the center vertical axis at the point where it intersects the line drawn in step 4.

      Example: What is the BSA for a 52-year-old man who is 170 cm tall and weighs 70 kg?

      Solution: Using the adult nomogram, place a dot on the left vertical axis at 170 cm and a dot on the right vertical axis at 70 kg. Connect the dots using a straightedge, and read the patient's BSA on the center vertical axis at the point where it intersects the straight line.

      Answer: BSA = 1.8 m^2

VI. Chemotherapy Dosing

A. BSA is frequently used for dosing chemotherapeutic drugs for cancer patients. There are many safety considerations that must be taken into account in prescribing, compounding, and administering antineoplastic drugs. Correct dosing is a critical concern. Dosing chemotherapeutic drugs is frequently done by establishing the patient's BSA (as outlined in the previous section) and then determining the dose by the ratio and proportion method.

B. Example: How many milligrams of paclitaxel would a 42-year-old, 131-lb., 65-inch-tall female patient receive if the intravenous adult dose for breast carcinoma is 175 mg per square meter of BSA repeated every 21 days?

Step 1: Use adult nomogram to determine the BSA: 1.65 m^2

Step 2: Determine dose by ratio and proportion method:
$175\ mg/m^2 = x/1.65\ m^2$
$x = 289\ mg$

VII. Sample Questions

1. Solve the following using the principles of ratio and proportion:

   a. 1 tbsp. = 15 mL = ________tsp.

   b. 1 fluid oz. = 30 mL = ________tsp. = ________tbsp.

   c. 1 pt. = ________fluid oz. = ________mL = ________tbsp. = ________tsp.

2. A child's amoxicillin dose is 20 mg/kg/day in divided doses every 8 hours.

   a. This dose could also be written as 20 mg/________lb./day.

   b. How many grams of amoxicillin would a 44-lb. child receive daily?

   c. How many milligrams would this child receive per dose?

   d. Amoxicillin is available as an oral suspension (125 mg/5 mL). How many teaspoonsful should this child receive per dose?

   e. How many teaspoonsful should this child receive per day?

   f. How many milliliters would you dispense for 10 days of therapy?

   g. How many fluid ounces would you dispense for 10 days of therapy?

   h. How many doses would the patient receive in 7 days?

3. How many milliliters of a liquid laxative should be dispensed if the dose prescribed is for 1 tbsp. q.i.d. for 3 days?

4. Flow rate calculations

   a. If the flow rate for normal saline (NS) is 30 drops per minute over 6 hours, how many milliliters of NS would the patient receive (*assume 18 gtt./mL*)?

   b. How many grams of NaCl would be administered (NS = 0.9 g of NaCl per 100 mL)?

5. A drug is administered by infusion at the rate of 1 mcg/lb./min. for anesthesia. If a 90-kg man is to receive a total of 0.85 mg of the drug:

   a. How long should the drug be infused?

   b. If the drug is available in a strength of 2 mg/5 mL, how many milliliters would the patient receive per minute?

   c. How many total milliliters would the patient receive?

6. How many milliliters of an injection containing 90 mg/mL of a drug should be administered to a 50-lb. child if the recommended dose is 6 mg per pound of body weight?

7. How many 125 mg antifungal tablets should be dispensed for a 100-lb. patient to provide a 30-day supply if the normal daily dose is 5 mg per pound of body weight?

8. An injectable antibiotic has a dose of 10 mg per kilogram of body weight. How many milliliters of a 125 mg/mL injection should be administered to a child weighing 66 lb.?

9. How many milliliters of digoxin injection 0.5 mg/2 mL would provide a 100 mcg dose?

10. A solution of sodium fluoride contains 1.1 mg/mL and has a dose of 15 drops. How many milligrams of sodium fluoride are in each dose if the dispensing dropper calibrates at 28 gtt./mL?

11. How many grams of diazepam will a patient receive in a week if he takes a 10 mg tablet t.i.d.?

12. a. How many teaspoonful doses can a patient receive from a 6 fluid oz. bottle of cough syrup?

    b. For how long will this bottle of cough syrup last if the patient takes 1 dose every 4 hours?

13. How many milliliters of digoxin elixir 50 mcg/mL would provide a 0.25 mg dose?

14. a. A patient is to receive ampicillin 250 mg q.i.d. for 10 days. How many capsules should be dispensed?

    b. If this prescription costs $16.80, how much does a dose cost?

15. a. How many milliliters of amoxicillin 250 mg/5 mL should be dispensed if the directions are to take 1 tsp. t.i.d. for 10 days?

    b. How many days will this dispensed volume last if the physician changes the directions to read: Take 1 1/2 tsp. b.i.d.?

16. a. If the dose of a medication for an infant is 3 mg/lb., how much would a 12-lb. baby receive?

    b. How much of a drug available in an 8 mg/mL strength would provide the appropriate dose for this baby?

17. a. How many tablespoonful doses of potassium chloride can a patient receive from a 1 pt. bottle of potassium chloride?

    b. If the potassium chloride contains 10 g of potassium in every 100 mL, how many grams would a single dose contain?

    c. How many milligrams of potassium chloride would this 1 pt. bottle contain?

18. a. A patient is to receive a liter of NS over 8 hours. How many milliliters will the patient receive each hour?

    b. How many drops per minute would this patient receive if the IV set delivers 10 gtt./mL?

19. a. What is the BSA of a 65-year-old patient who is 67 inches tall and weighs 152 lb.?

    b. If the recommended dose of a chemotherapy drug for this patient is 400 mcg/m^2, what would the dose be in milligrams?

The **Answer Key** appears In **Section VIII**.

Notes:

Nomogram for Adults

Determination of body surface from height and mass[1]

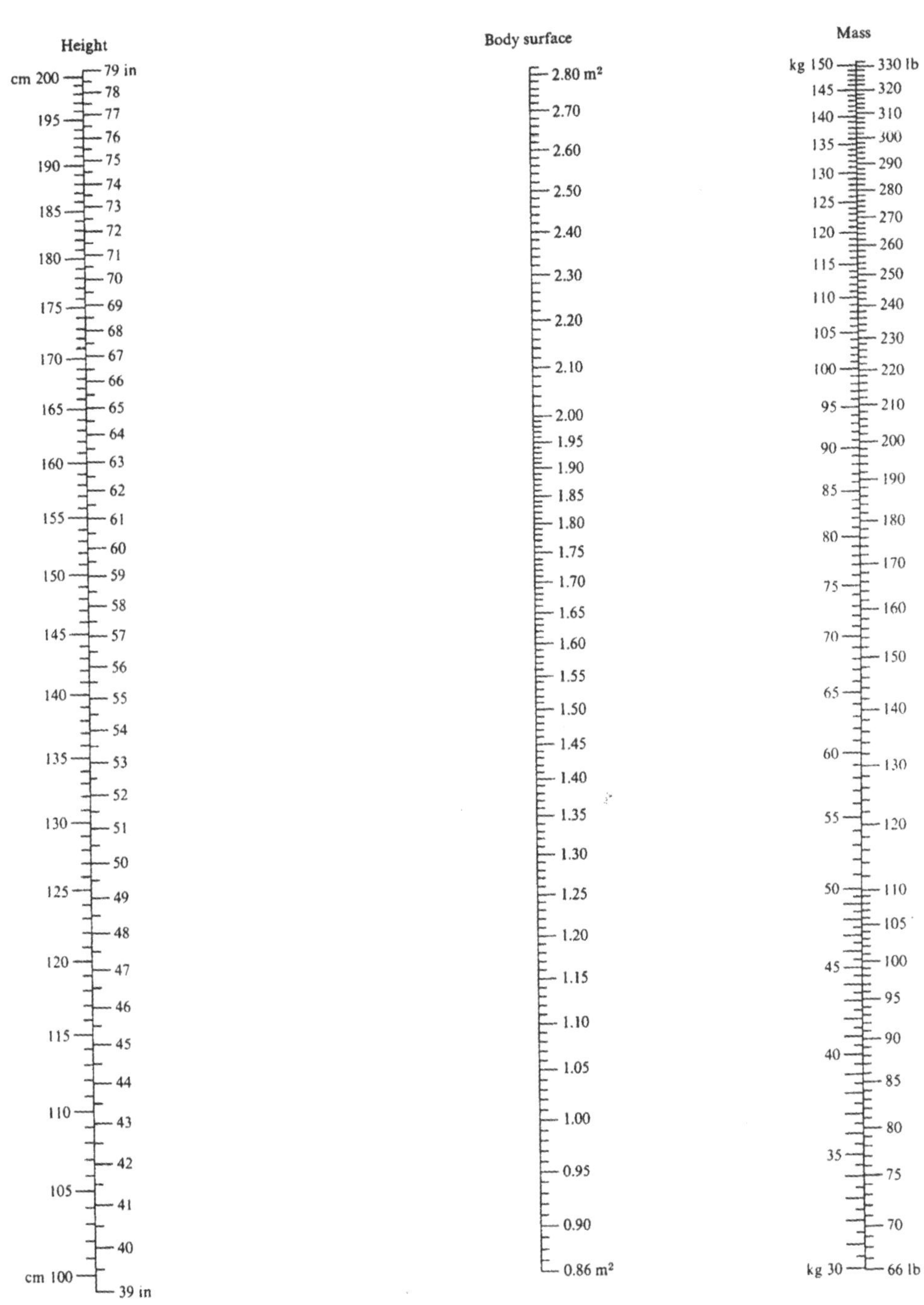

---

[1] From the formula of Du Bois and Du Bois, *Arch Intern Med*, 17, 863 (1916): $S = M^{0.425} \times H^{0.725} \times 71.84$, or $\log S = \log M \times 0.425 + \log H \times 0.725 + 1.8564$ (S = body surface in cm^2, M = mass in kg, H = height in cm).

Source: C. Lentner, Ed., *Geigy Scientific Tables*, 8th ed, vol 1, Basel: Ciba-Geigy; 1981: 226-7.

Chapter 18

Concentrations

I. Reducing and Enlarging Formulas

A. Pharmacists and technicians often have to prepare larger and/or smaller quantities than a recipe might call for. Recipes can be reduced or enlarged by creating a factor or using the principles of ratio and proportion.

1. Example: Recipe on a box for eight medium-size pancakes

Pancake mix	1 cup
Water	1/2 cup
Milk	1/4 cup
Eggs	2
Vegetable oil	2 tsp.

a. How much milk would be needed to make 16 pancakes?

b. How many eggs are needed to make four pancakes?

These problems can be solved by creating a factor using the amount the recipe calls for as a denominator and the amount desired as the numerator. Multiply this factor times each component in the recipe to "reduce" or "enlarge" the formula. In the above examples, the calculation would be:

$$\frac{\text{16 pancakes}}{\text{8 pancakes}} = 2\ (\text{1/4 cup of milk}) = \text{1/2 cup of milk}$$

$$\frac{\text{4 pancakes}}{\text{8 pancakes}} = 1/2\ (\text{2 eggs}) = \text{1 egg}$$

These problems can also be solved by using the principles of ratio and proportion:

$$\frac{\text{1/4 cup of milk}}{\text{8 pancakes}} = \frac{x}{\text{16 pancakes}} \qquad x = \text{1/2 cup}$$

$$\frac{2 \text{ eggs}}{8 \text{ pancakes}} = \frac{x}{4 \text{ pancakes}} \qquad x = 1 \text{ egg}$$

II. Concentrations and Dilutions

A. Concentration may be expressed as a percentage. There are three types of percentages:

1. Weight-in-weight (w/w) percentage preparations

   a. Use weight-in-weight percentage when the final product is a solid (e.g., powder, ointment) and the component for which you are measuring the percentage is also a solid. Units in the numerator and denominator must be the same (e.g., lb./lb., gr./gr.).

      (1) Example: 2 g of sulfur in 100 g of a final ointment would be 2 g/100 g = 0.02 = 2% w/w

2. Volume-in-volume (v/v) percentage preparations

   a. Use volume-in-volume percentage when the final product is a liquid (e.g., solution) and the component for which you are measuring the percentage is also a liquid. Units in the numerator must be the same as in the denominator (e.g., mL/mL, pt./pt.).

      (1) Example: 5 mL of a flavoring oil in 100 mL of mouthwash would be 5 mL/100 mL = 0.05 = 5% v/v

3. Weight-in-volume (w/v) percentage preparations

   a. Use weight-in-volume percentage when the final product is a liquid, as indicated by the (v) in the denominator (e.g., suspensions), and the component for which you are measuring the percentage is a solid, as indicated by the (w) in the numerator. In w/v percentages, the numerator is always expressed in grams and the denominator is always expressed in milliliters. This differs from w/w and v/v percentages, where the units must be the same for both the numerator and denominator.

      (1) Example: 17 g of drug K in 100 mL of a final solution would be 17 g/100 mL = 0.17 or 17% w/v

B. Ratio strength preparations

1. Ratios are another way of expressing percent, or parts per 100. For example:

   a. A 5% w/w product is 5 parts per 100 parts, or 5:100.

   b. A 20% v/v solution is 20 parts per 100 parts, or 20:100 (this could mean 20 mL of drug in 100 mL of solution, or 20 L in 100 L, etc.).

c. A 15% w/v solution means 15 g of drug in 100 mL of solution, or 15:100.

2. Ratio strength calculations are performed like percentage calculations.

   a. Example: 5% w/v = 5 g in 100 mL = 1 g in 20 mL = 1:20

3. Ratios should always be reduced so that the number "1" is written to the left of the colon (e.g., 1:100, not 2:200, even though these ratios are equal).

   a. Example: 3:15 could also be written:

$$\frac{3}{15} = \frac{1}{x}$$

x = 5, so 3:15 = 1:5

C. Stock solutions

1. Stock solutions are concentrated solutions used to make weaker strength solutions.

D. Diluting stock preparations

1. A dilution involves taking a certain percentage solution and adding a 0% diluent to decrease the percentage concentration.

   a. Example: How much water would you add to 100 mL of a 15% potassium chloride solution to get a 5% final product?

   This problem cannot be solved by simple ratio and proportion because you are looking for an inverse relationship (i.e., the more solvent we add, the *lower* the percentage). Instead, use this formula:

   (old volume)(old %) = (new volume)(new percent), which is also expressed as:
   (O.V.)(O.%) = (N.V.)(N.%)

   Step 1: (100 mL)(15%) = (x)(5%)

   Step 2: $$\frac{(100 \text{ mL})(15\%)}{(5\%)} = x \qquad x = 300 \text{ mL}$$

   Note: 300 mL is the final and total dilution you have made by adding 100 mL of 15% KCl to a certain volume of water. It is not the amount of water added.

   Step 3: 300 mL final solution – 100 mL of 15% = 200 mL of H_2O added

III. Alligation Methods

A. Alligation alternate method

1. Basic principles

   a. Use the alligation alternate method for making dilutions when the diluent is zero percent or higher. (Previous dilution examples used a zero percent diluent only.)

   b. This method determines how many "parts" of each diluent will be needed to get the % final product.

   c. "Parts" can have any value (e.g., mL, gr., pinches).

   d. The "parts" added together will equal the total parts of the final product.

   e. You can only dilute to an intermediate percent. For example, you cannot add 10% to 20% and get a percent higher than 20% or lower than 10%. The final product will be somewhere between 10% and 20%.

2. Examples

   a. If you need a 10% sulfur ointment and have only 5% and 20% ointments available, use the alligation alternate method to determine how many "parts" of each will be needed to get the 10% final product.

   First, find the absolute differences between the desired and the existing percentages:

   (1) Subtract 5% from 10% to get 5 parts.
   (2) Subtract 10% from 20% to get 10 parts.

   Next, apply the part values to the alternate percentages to set up a ratio:

   (3) The ratio is 5 parts of 20%:10 parts of 5%.

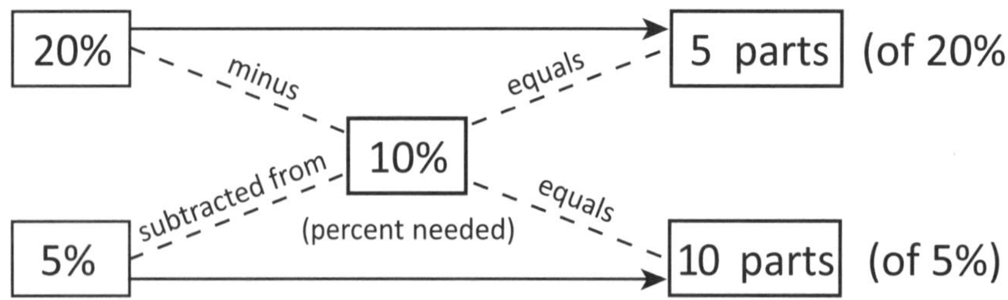

b. Using data from the previous example, prepare 1 kg of the 10% sulfur ointment.

Step 1: Add the parts, i.e., 5 + 10 = 15 parts (*Note:* The 15 parts represent the total quantities of the 20% and 5% ointments that are being combined. The "new" product, which is a 10% ointment, is equal to 15 parts.)

Step 2: 15 parts/1000 g = 10 parts/x
x = 667 g (of 5% ointment)

Step 3: 15 parts/1000 g = 5 parts/x
x = 333 g (of 20% ointment)

Note: Step 3 can be skipped by simply subtracting 667 from 1000.

Answer: To compound 1000 g of 10%, add 667 g of 5% ointment to 333 g of 20% ointment.

B. Alligation medial method

1. Use the alligation medial method to obtain the average strength of a mixture of two or more substances whose concentration and percent strength are already known. This method can also be used to check an alligation alternate problem.

2. Example from the mixture in A.2. above:

Step 1: 5 parts × 20% = 100 parts %
10 parts × 5% = 50 parts %

15 parts 150 parts %

Step 2: $\frac{150 \text{ parts } \%}{15 \text{ parts } \%} = 10\%$

IV. Milliequivalents

A. Definitions

1. Electrolytes

a. Electrolytes are important for many bodily functions that require electrical activity, such as nerve conduction and muscle contraction. Electrolyte replacement is usually ordered in units of milligrams or milliequivalents.

2. Milliequivalents

   a. A milliequivalent (mEq) is equal to the millimoles of H^+ or OH^- that will react with 1 mmol of an ion or compound. When an atom has the valence of "one," a milliequivalent (mEq) is simply equal to the atomic weight (AW) of the atom (e.g., Na^+ = 23, so there are 23 mg/mEq).

   b. Example: A molecule like sodium chloride (NaCl) has a molecular weight (MW) of 58.5. Therefore, 1 mEq = 58.5 mg, and when the molecule dissociates, it yields 1 mEq Na^+ and 1 mEq Cl^-.

B. Converting to milliequivalents

1. Example: If a solution contains 10 g of potassium chloride (KCl), how many mEq of K^+ does it contain? The AW of K^+ = 39 and the AW of Cl^- = 35.5. Therefore, the MW of KCl = 74.5.

   74.5 mg = 1 mEq
   10 g = 10,000 mg
   74.5 mg/1 mEq = 10,000 mg/x = 134 mEq

C. Divalent and trivalent ions

1. Sometimes you will have an exception to the rule when you have divalent ions (e.g., Mg^{++}, Ca^{++}) and trivalent ions (e.g., Al^{+++}). In most cases when magnesium or calcium is involved in the molecule, 1 mEq is equal to 1/2 the MW. With aluminum-containing products, 1 mEq is equal to 1/3 the MW.

   a. Example: Calcium chloride ($CaCl_2$) AW of Ca^{++} = 40 AW of Cl^- = 35.5
   40 + 35.5 + 35.5 = 111 mg total weight
   1 mEq = 111/2 (i.e., valence) = 55.5 mg

V. Dry Powders for Reconstitution

A. Many unstable medications are packaged as dry powders and must be dissolved in a solvent prior to dispensing. The most frequently encountered drugs requiring reconstitution are antibiotics.

B. In most cases, reconstitutions can be accomplished in three steps:

1. Establish how much drug is in the vial or bottle.

2. Calculate the powder volume displacement.

3. Solve the problem using ratio and proportion.

a. Example 1: The label on a vial reads, "Add 9.2 mL of diluent to the vial to get 10 mL of a 100 mg/mL solution for injection." How many milliliters of the reconstituted solution would provide a 250 mg dose?

(1) Step 1:

$$\frac{100\text{ mg}}{1\text{ mL}} = \frac{x}{10\text{ mL}}$$

x = 1000 mg per vial

(2) Step 2: not required at this point

(3) Step 3:

$$\frac{1000\text{ mg}}{10\text{ mL}} = \frac{250\text{ mg}}{x}$$

x = 2.5 mL

Note: This problem can also be solved by using the per-milliliter concentration of 100 mg/mL:

$$\frac{100\text{ mL}}{1\text{ mL}} = \frac{250\text{ mg}}{x}$$

b. How much of the diluted solution for injection in Example 1 would you measure to get the 250 mg dose if you accidentally reconstituted with 11 mL of diluent?

(1) Step 1: 1000 mg per vial

(2) Step 2: If 9.2 mL of diluent, when mixed with the powder, yields 10 mL, then the powder volume displacement is 0.8 mL (i.e., 10 – 9.2 = 0.8).

(3) Step 3: 0.8 mL of powder + 11 mL of diluent = 11.8 mL

$$\frac{1000\text{ mg}}{11.8\text{ mL}} = \frac{250\text{ mg}}{x}$$

x = 2.95 mL

c. Example 2: You have been directed to reconstitute a 5 million unit vial of Drug A to a concentration of 500,000 units/mL. The drug has a powder volume displacement of 0.002 L. How many milliliters of diluent will you need to add to this vial?

(1) Step 1: 5,000,000 units per vial

(2) Step 2: 2 mL (given as 0.002 L)

(3) Step 3: If you want 500,000 units per 1 mL, then

$$\frac{500{,}000 \text{ units}}{1 \text{ mL}} = \frac{5{,}000{,}000 \text{ units}}{x}$$

x = 10 mL (this is the total volume of the vial)
10 mL total volume – 2 mL powder
volume displacement = 8 mL of diluent to be added

VI. Sample Questions

1. Answer the next 3 questions using the following recipe for benzyl benzoate lotion:

Benzyl benzoate	250 mL
Triethanolamine	5 g
Oleic acid	20 g
Purified water to make	1000 mL

   a. How many grams of triethanolamine are required to make 1 gal. of benzyl benzoate lotion? How many milligrams?

   b. How many grains of oleic acid are required to make 1 pt. of benzyl benzoate lotion?

   c. How many teaspoonsful of benzyl benzoate are there in 100 mL of the lotion?

2. a. What percentage of sulfur would be in a product that contains 2 g of sulfur in 120 g of ointment?

   b. How many milligrams of sulfur would be contained in 1 g of ointment?

3. What percentage of sulfur would be in a product containing 20 g of sulfur in 1 lb. of ointment?

4. a. What percentage sulfur ointment would result from *adding* 50 g of sulfur to 120 g of petrolatum?

   b. What is the percentage of petrolatum in the ointment?

5. Ninety grams of 25% zinc oxide ointment would contain how many grams of zinc oxide?

6. a. What percentage of flavoring oil would be in a mouthwash that has 2 tbsp. of oil in 1 pt. of mouthwash?

   b. How many milliliters of oil would be in 60 mL of the mouthwash?

7. Calculate the percentage of a preparation containing 7 g of drug K in 5 fluid oz. of a final product.

8. a. Calculate the percentage of a preparation containing 1 lb. of drug K in 1 gal. of a final product.

   b. What is the ratio strength of the final product?

9. a. One pint of a 10% w/v suspension would contain _______g of drug.

   b. One teaspoonful of this suspension would be what percent w/v?

10. One quart of a 1:50 w/v solution would be _______% and contain _______g of active ingredient.

11. a. How many milligrams per milliliter would be in a 6% w/v solution?

    b. What is the ratio strength of this solution?

12. A solution containing 2000 mg of a drug in 8 fluid oz. would be a ______% w/v solution or a ______ ratio strength solution and contain ______mg/mL.

13. a. Convert 6:720 into a correctly written ratio strength.

    b. Express this value as a percentage strength.

14. a. What is the resulting percentage of benzalkonium chloride obtained from diluting 1 fluid oz. of 17% benzalkonium chloride to 1 pt.?

    b. What is the final ratio strength?

    c. How many milligrams per milliliter are in the final dilution?

    d. How many grams per teaspoonful are in the initial 17% solution?

    e. What is the percentage strength of 1 tsp. of the 17% solution *added* to 1 tbsp. of water?

    f. How many grains of benzalkonium chloride are in 1 fluid oz. of 17% benzalkonium chloride?

    g. How many grains of benzalkonium chloride are in the final 1 pt. dilution?

    h. If 100 mL of a 1:200 drug solution is diluted to 1 L, what is the final ratio strength?

    i. How many milligrams per teaspoonful doses are in the final dilution in question 14h?

15. a. Can you mix a 20% ointment with a 5% ointment to make a 10% ointment?

    b. If yes, how many grams of each component would be required to make 1 lb. of a 10% ointment?

    c. If yes, how many grams of 10% ointment could be made if you had only 30 g of 20% and plenty of 5%?

16. a. Can you mix a 20% ointment with a 15% ointment to make a 10% ointment?

    b. If yes, how many grams of each component would be required to make 1 lb. of a 10% ointment?

    c. If yes, how many grams of 10% ointment could be made if you had only 1 oz. of 20% and plenty of 15%?

17. A liter of NS (0.9% sodium chloride) would contain ______g of sodium chloride and ______mEq of sodium. (AW of Na^+ = 23; AW of Cl^- = 35.5)

18. a. If 100 mL of a solution contains 10 mEq of KCl, what is the percentage strength of potassium chloride? (MW of KCl = 74.5)

    b. How many milligrams of KCl are required to prepare 1 L of this solution?

19. How many milliequivalents of calcium are in a tablespoonful of a solution containing 250 mg of calcium chloride ($CaCl_2$)? (AW of Ca^{++} = 40; Cl^- = 35.5)

20. What is the percentage strength of calcium chloride in the solution in the previous question?

21. How many milliequivalents of aluminum are in 1 g of aluminum hydroxide Al $(OH)_3$? (AW of Al = 27; O = 16; H = 1)

22. Answer the next 3 questions using the following prescription for ampicillin suspension:

    Rx Ampicillin 250 mg/5 mL
    Sig.: 1 tsp. q.i.d. × 10 d

    a. How many milliliters would you dispense?

    b. Assume that the instructions on the bottle of dry ampicillin powder for reconstitution require the addition of 160 mL of water to obtain the volume needed to correctly fill the prescription. What volume will the drug powder account for?

    c. How many grams of ampicillin will the patient receive in 1 week?

23. The prescription below is a formula for 1 capsule to be extemporaneously compounded. How many 30 mg codeine sulfate tablets would be required to make 50 of these capsules?

Rx Acetylsalicylic acid 325 mg
Codeine sulfate 5 mg
Sig.: 1 capsule q.4h p.r.n. pain

24. a. How many 250 mg erythromycin tablets would be required to compound the prescription below?

Rx E-Mycin 2%
Alcohol q.s. 150 mL

b. What is the ratio strength of 1 tsp. of this prescription?

c. How many milligrams are in each milliliter of this prescription?

25. The instructions on a vial for reconstitution state, "Add 12.8 mL of diluent to make 15 mL of a 500 mg/mL solution." You have on hand only 10 mL of the diluent, which you use for reconstitution.

a. How much drug is in the vial?

b. Does the total amount of drug in the vial change according to the amount of diluent added?

c. Does the amount of drug per milliliter vary with the amount of diluent added?

d. What is the powder volume displacement of the drug?

e. How many milliliters of the reconstituted solution, according to instructions on the vial, would provide a 2 g dose of the drug?

f. How many milliliters of the reconstituted solution made with 10 mL of diluent would provide a 2 g dose of the drug?

26. a. What is the percent strength of coal tar in a mixture of 1/2 kg of 3% coal tar ointment and 1500 g of 10% coal tar ointment?

b. What is the ratio strength of the coal tar mixture?

c. How many grams of coal tar are in 1 lb. of this mixture?

d. Can a 1:50 coal tar ointment be prepared by mixing the 3% and 10% coal tar ointments?

e. How many grams of coal tar should be added to the coal tar mixture to obtain an ointment containing 18% coal tar?

The **Answer Key** appears in **Section VIII**.

Notes:

Chapter 19

Pharmacy Business Calculations

I. Determining Charges for Prescriptions and Medication Orders

A. Cost

1. Cost is the total amount paid for an item or items received, as noted on an invoice.

   a. Example: The invoice states that you purchased 1/2 dozen mugs at $1.50 each, for a total of $9.00.

$$6 \times \$1.50 \text{ each} = \$9 \quad \text{or} \quad \frac{1 \text{ mug}}{\$1.50} = \frac{6 \text{ mugs}}{x}$$

B. Selling price

1. The selling price is 100% of the amount you will receive for the sale of an item (this includes your cost plus whatever amount you want as a profit).

C. Markup

1. Markup is the difference between the cost for a product and its actual selling price.

   Selling Price = Cost + Markup

2. Example: For 30 tablets costing $0.40 each for which you want to receive $0.10 profit per tablet:

   Selling Price = (30 × $0.40) + (30 × $0.10) = $12.00 + $3.00 = $15.00

D. Percent markup

1. Percent markup must be stated as either "percent markup on the selling price" or as "percent markup on the cost" to determine its true meaning. In retail practice, "percent markup" usually means percent of sales, not of cost.

a. From the previous example, percent markup based on cost would be:

$$\frac{\text{Markup}}{\text{Cost}} = \frac{\$3.00}{\$12.00} = 0.25 = 25\%$$

E. Percent gross profit

1. Percent gross profit is the percent markup based on the selling price, instead of the cost.

a. Example:

$$\text{Percent Gross Profit} = \frac{\text{Markup}}{\text{Selling Price}} = \frac{\$3.00}{\$15.00} = 0.20 = 20\%$$

F. Overhead

1. It is important to consider overhead to determine the true profit of a business. Overhead includes operating costs such as utilities, taxes, insurance, and technician salaries.

G. Net profit

1. Net profit can be defined as:

a. Selling Price – (Cost of Goods + Overhead)

H. Inventory

1. Inventory includes all items on hand and their total cost.

I. Turnover

1. Turnover refers to the number of times that merchandise is sold in a given length of time, normally 1 year.

II. Sample Questions

1. If you paid $0.20 per capsule for a bottle containing 100 capsules:

   a. What was the total cost of the bottle of capsules?

   b. If you wanted to make a $0.05 profit per capsule, what would be the selling price of 1 capsule?

   c. What would be the selling price of 30 capsules?

2. If a drug costs $50 and the selling price is $60:

   a. What is the markup?

   b. What is the percent markup based on cost?

   c. What is the percent gross profit?

3. A patient bought a humidifier for $65 that was initially purchased by the pharmacy from a medical supply company for $45.

   a. What is the markup on the humidifier?

   b. What is the percent markup on the humidifier based on selling price?

   c. What is the percent markup on the humidifier based on cost?

   d. What would be the selling price if the supplier's price was the same, but the pharmacy owner charged a 72% markup based on cost?

4. The markup on 40 antibiotic capsules is $10, and a patient pays $65 for the entire prescription.

   a. What is the acquisition cost of the capsules for the pharmacy?

   b. What is the average cost per capsule for the patient?

   c. What is the markup on each capsule?

   d. If the patient takes 1 capsule b.i.d., what will be the cost to the patient for a week of therapy?

   e. What is the percent markup on the prescription based on cost?

   f. What is the percent markup on the prescription based on selling price?

The **Answer Key** appears in **Section VIII**.

Notes:

Section VIII

Cumulative Practice Knowledge and Calculation Questions

William A. Hopkins Jr. and

Kristin W. Weitzel

Section VIII contains practice questions on:

- Pharmacy Technician Certification Examination (PTCE) content
- PTCE pharmaceutical calculations

Chapter 20

Practice Questions

1. Which of the following terms describes a route of administration?

    a. proprietary
    b. dosage form
    c. intranasal
    d. nutrient

2. How many milligrams of zephiran chloride are needed to prepare 3 L of 1:30,000 solution?

    a. 0.1
    b. 1
    c. 10
    d. 100

3. How many grams of bacitracin (500 units/g) should be used to prepare 1 kg of bacitracin ointment containing 250 units of bacitracin per gram?

    a. 100
    b. 500
    c. 1000
    d. 250,000

4. Patient profiles should be created for:

    a. Patients who have chronic diseases (e.g., diabetes, hypertension)
    b. Patients who have prescriptions filled at the pharmacy regularly
    c. Every patient who presents a prescription to the pharmacy
    d. Any patient who has had 3 or more prescriptions filled at the pharmacy within a 6-month period

5. How many milliliters of a drug would be needed to provide a 10,000 mcg dose from a vial containing 0.1 g/10 mL?

   a. 1
   b. 10
   c. 100
   d. 1000

6. How many milligrams of ephedrine sulfate should be used to prepare the following prescription?

   Rx   Sol. Ephedrine sulfate 1/4 %   30 mL
        Sig.: Use as directed

   a. 0.075
   b. 0.75
   c. 7.5
   d. 75

7. What is the generic name for Keflex®?

   a. Cefadroxil
   b. Cefixime
   c. Cephalexin
   d. Ceftazidime

8. An order is received to administer 5 mEq of potassium acetate per hour. The bag of intravenous fluid contains 30 mEq/L. How many drops per minute would be needed to provide the prescribed dose using a set that delivers 15 gtt./mL?

   a. 3
   b. 12
   c. 42
   d. 167

9. How many liters of a 0.9% aqueous sodium chloride solution can be made from 60 g of NaCl?

   a. 6.67
   b. 66.7
   c. 667
   d. 6667

10. How many grams of a 5% sulfur ointment must be mixed with 180 g of 20% sulfur ointment to prepare an 8% sulfur ointment?

    a. 45
    b. 90
    c. 180
    d. 720

11. If 5 mL of diluent are added to a vial containing 2 g of a drug for injection resulting in a final volume of 5.8 mL, what is the concentration in milligrams per milliliter of the drug in the reconstituted solution?

    a. 0.3
    b. 345
    c. 400
    d. 2035

12. Which prescription instructions would require 17 tablets to be dispensed?

    a. One tab. p.o. b.i.d. × 7 d
    b. One tab. a.c. & h.s. × 4 d
    c. One tab. t.i.d. × 3 d; 1 tab. b.i.d. × 3 d; 1 tab. q.d. × 3 d
    d. Two tab. b.i.d. × 2 d; 2 tab. q.d. × 3 d; 1 tab. q.d. × 3 d

13. Which of the following is not considered a dosage form?

    a. Powder
    b. Inhalation
    c. Paste
    d. Lotion

14. How many milliliters per hour would be required to infuse a dopamine dose of 5 mcg/kg/min. to a patient weighing 220 lb. if the dopamine is provided by a bag containing 800 mg/500 mL?

    a. 18.75
    b. 30.35
    c. 100.45
    d. 528.34

15. A physician prescribes 10 mg of a drug per kilogram of body weight once daily for 21 days for a patient weighing 264 lb. How many 200 mg tablets of the drug are required daily?

    a. 2
    b. 4
    c. 6
    d. 12

16. How many grams of potassium permanganate are required to prepare 2 qt. of 1:750 solution of potassium permanganate?

    a. 0.05
    b. 0.13
    c. 1.28
    d. 13

17. When the physician's instructions indicate that a drug should be taken sublingually, what directions might be included on the prescription label?

   a. Change the patch every 12 hours.
   b. Chew the medication thoroughly.
   c. Place the medication under the tongue until it dissolves.
   d. Use 0.5 mL in 2 mL of normal saline every 4 hours as needed.

18. The formula for zinc gelatin is:

Glycerin	400 g
Gelatin	150 g
Zinc oxide	100 g
Purified water	350 g

   How much glycerin would be required to prepare 1 lb. of zinc gelatin?

   a. 182 g
   b. 192 g
   c. 519 g
   d. 1000 g

19. Which drug is used to treat patients with diabetes?

   a. Metformin
   b. Glucotrol
   c. Actos
   d. All of the above

20. How many 1/2 pt. bottles can be filled from a 2 gal. container of 10% potassium chloride?

   a. 16
   b. 32
   c. 64
   d. 128

21. A complete patient profile should include all of the following except:

   a. Nonprescription medications the patient is currently using
   b. Patient's annual income for reimbursement/payment information
   c. The brand name or manufacturer of the drug dispensed to fill the prescription
   d. Physical limitations and sociological factors specific to the patient

22. What is the percent alcohol contained in a mixture of 90 mL of elixir phenobarbital (14% alcohol), 100 mL of water, and 40 mL of high alcoholic elixir (78% alcohol)?

    a. 8%
    b. 19%
    c. 26%
    d. 64%

23. The technician must notify the pharmacist before modifying the patient profile in all cases except:

    a. The patient has experienced a stroke and has been prescribed a different antihypertensive medication.
    b. The strength or dosage of insulin differs from the patient's previous prescription.
    c. The patient is now covered by a new medical/prescription insurance company.
    d. The patient has become pregnant since the last prescription was filled.

24. If the dose of a drug is 35 mg/kg/day in 6 divided doses, how much would be given in each dose to a 38-lb. child?

    a. 17.3 mg
    b. 60.4 mg
    c. 101 mg
    d. 604 mg

25. How many micrograms of digoxin would be contained in 0.75 mL of an ampule labeled 0.5 mg/2 mL?

    a. 0.188
    b. 3.6
    c. 13.2
    d. 187.5

26. Patient profile information must include all of the following except:

    a. The pharmacist's signature confirming each item of information listed
    b. Patient's prescription history
    c. Patient allergies
    d. Reimbursement information

27. How many grams of potassium chloride are used in making 1 L of a solution containing 3 mEq of potassium per teaspoonful? (MW of KCl = 74.5)

    a. 44.7
    b. 74.5
    c. 223.5
    d. 44,700

28. How many milliliters of 20% merthiolate solution should be diluted with water to make 600 mL of a 0.5% merthiolate solution?

    a. 15
    b. 178
    c. 580
    d. 24,000

29. Using proper aseptic technique requires that all intravenous solutions must be:

    a. Filtered prior to dispensing
    b. Prepared in a laminar flow hood
    c. Administered in at least 50 mL of normal saline
    d. Refrigerated immediately after compounding

30. How many grams of yellow mercuric oxide must be *added* to 30 g of 1% yellow mercuric oxide ointment to prepare a 5% ointment?

    a. 0.8
    b. 1.26
    c. 28.9
    d. 713

31. An elixir is to contain 500 mcg of an alkaloid in each tablespoonful dose. How many milligrams of alkaloid would be required to prepare a liter of the elixir?

    a. 3.33
    b. 7.5
    c. 33.3
    d. 33,333

32. A prescription calls for 500 mg of tetracaine hydrochloride. If tetracaine hydrochloride costs $24.50 per 3 g, what is the cost of the quantity necessary to prepare the prescription?

    a. $1.25
    b. $2.85
    c. $4.08
    d. $147.72

33. How many milliliters of ampicillin 250 mg/5 mL should be dispensed to fill a prescription for 500 mg q.i.d. times 10 days?

    a. 100
    b. 150
    c. 200
    d. 400

34. An example of injectable drug cross-contamination that could cause a potentially fatal reaction would be:

    a. Cefamandole-cefazolin
    b. Gentamicin-amikacin
    c. Ampicillin-aminophylline
    d. Meperidine-codeine

35. All prescription labels must include:

    a. Trade name of the medication
    b. Generic name of the medication
    c. Address of the patient
    d. Expiration date

36. How many milliliters of 95% alcohol should be mixed with 30% alcohol to make 2000 mL of a 40% alcohol solution?

    a. 31
    b. 108
    c. 222
    d. 308

37. How many grams of benzethonium chloride should be used in preparing 4 pt. of a 1:1000 solution of benzethonium chloride?

    a. 1.92
    b. 3.86
    c. 20
    d. 38

38. How many milliequivalents of potassium gluconate are there in 2 tbsp. of a 30% potassium gluconate solution? (MW potassium gluconate = 234; valence = 1)

    a. 21.65
    b. 38.46
    c. 390
    d. 9000

39. The dose of a drug for a 150-lb. patient is 280 mg. How many milliliters of a product containing 180 mg/tsp. would provide the appropriate dose?

    a. 4.9
    b. 7.8
    c. 12.7
    d. 18.2

40. Which of the following laws required the use of child-resistant packaging for drug products?

a. Durham-Humphrey
b. Controlled Substances Act
c. Poison Prevention Act
d. Pure Food and Drug Act

41. The principle behind the use of the horizontal laminar airflow hood is:

a. Air from the sterile compounding room is pumped directly through the hood horizontally to minimize contamination from microorganisms.
b. Filtered air flows from the hood toward the operator to provide a relatively clean work area.
c. Filtered air is provided in straight, parallel lines, flowing downward.
d. The operator is protected from the possible hazardous effects of cytotoxic agents.

42. How many milliliters of a 0.5% sodium sulfate solution should be mixed with a 5% sodium sulfate solution to make a liter of 2% solution?

a. 250
b. 333
c. 500
d. 667

43. There are 18 g of an expectorant in a liter of a cough syrup. How many grains of expectorant are contained in a teaspoonful dose of the cough syrup?

a. 0.09
b. 1.38
c. 5.84
d. 90

44. How many capsules, each containing 1 3/8 gr. of a drug, can be filled completely from a 28 g bottle of the drug?

a. 24
b. 32
c. 313
d. 431

45. If 4 fluid oz. of a solution cost $8.75, how much would a tablespoonful cost?

a. $0.36
b. $1.09
c. $4.38
d. $6.25

46. How many milliequivalents of potassium are in 2 g of potassium penicillin V if the molecular weight is 389 and the valence is 1?

    a. 5.14
    b. 78.2
    c. 154.6
    d. 389.3

47. What would be the infusion rate for a 50 mg/mL magnesium sulfate solution to provide 1.2 g/hr.?

    a. 0.4 mL/min.
    b. 2.5 mL/min.
    c. 20 mL/min.
    d. 24 mL/min.

48. A neonate in the nursery weighing 5 lb. 8 oz. requires 2.5 mg/kg of gentamicin. How many milliliters of solution containing 20 mg/mL should be administered?

    a. 0.029
    b. 0.31
    c. 2.5
    d. 6.3

49. A solution contains 5 mEq of calcium per 50 mL. How many milligrams of calcium would be contained in a liter of this solution? (AW calcium = 40; valence = 2)

    a. 20
    b. 100
    c. 2000
    d. 4000

50. How many milligrams of benzocaine are needed to prepare the following prescription?

Rx	Glycerin	2.5%
	Benzocaine	2%
	Hydrophilic ung. q.s.	60 g

    a. 1.2
    b. 12
    c. 120
    d. 1200

51. How many grains of ephedrine are left in a 437.5 gr. bottle of ephedrine after compounding 400 capsules each containing 3/8 gr. of ephedrine?

a. 28.5
b. 73.2
c. 150.8
d. 287.5

52. Heroin has no accepted medical use and an extremely high potential for abuse. It is classified as which of the following under the Controlled Substances Act?

a. Schedule I
b. Schedule II
c. Schedule III
d. Schedule IV

53. The instructions on a nafcillin vial say to add 3.4 mL of sterile water to the 1 g vial resulting in 4.1 mL of solution. How many milliliters would provide a 675 mg dose?

a. 0.36
b. 1.92
c. 2.31
d. 2.77

54. Assume in the previous question that you accidentally used 4.3 mL of sterile water to reconstitute the 1 g vial of nafcillin. How many milliliters of this new solution would provide the 675 mg dose?

a. 0.7
b. 2.8
c. 3.4
d. 4.3

55. How many milliliters of a 0.1% solution can be made from 75 mg of a chemical?

a. 10 mL
b. 75 mL
c. 100 mL
d. 750 mL

56. A compounded ointment requires it to be heated to 65°C. What would this reading be on a Fahrenheit thermometer?

a. 18
b. 68
c. 149
d. 172

57. Which of the following automated computer warnings is intended to alert the pharmacist or technician to a potential problem with a prescription?

    a. FDA alerts
    b. DUR or DUE alerts
    c. PPI alerts
    d. Medication Guide alerts

58. One gram of dextrose provides 3.4 calories. How many calories would be provided by a liter of a 50% dextrose solution?

    a. 1.7
    b. 17
    c. 170
    d. 1700

59. How many grams of coal tar are needed to compound 1 lb. of this prescription?

Rx	Coal tar	2 g
	Zinc oxide paste q.s.	60 g

    a. 2.3
    b. 15.1
    c. 16.2
    d. 21.6

60. An intravenous solution containing 20,000 units of heparin in 500 mL of 0.45% sodium chloride solution is to be infused to provide 1000 units of heparin per hour. How many drops per minute should be infused to deliver the desired dose if the IV set calibrates at 15 gtt./mL?

    a. 0.42
    b. 6
    c. 16
    d. 32

61. How many colchicine tablets containing 600 mcg each can be prepared from 40 g of colchicine?

    a. 66
    b. 666
    c. 6666
    d. 66,666

62. How many grams of a 5% benzocaine ointment can be prepared by diluting 1 lb. of 20% benzocaine ointment with white petrolatum?

    a. 129
    b. 642
    c. 735
    d. 1816

63. How many milligrams of pilocarpine nitrate are required to prepare 15 mL of an ophthalmic solution containing 0.25% pilocarpine nitrate?

   a. 0.61
   b. 18.2
   c. 37.5
   d. 380.9

64. How many 2.25 g sodium chloride tablets would be required to prepare 5 L of a 0.9% solution of sodium chloride?

   a. 20
   b. 70
   c. 100
   d. 2000

65. From the following formula, determine how many grams of calcium carbonate would be required to prepare 1 kg of the powder:

Magnesium oxide	1 part
Calcium carbonate	6 parts
Sodium bicarbonate	8 parts

   a. 0.1
   b. 30
   c. 400
   d. 750

66. Prochlorperazine injection is available in 10 mL multiple dose vials containing 5 mg/mL. How many 2.5 mg doses can be withdrawn from a single vial?

   a. 4
   b. 5
   c. 20
   d. 40

67. How many milliliters of water should be *added* to a quart of 10% boric acid solution to make a 3% solution?

   a. 1120
   b. 1600
   c. 2240
   d. 3200

68. Which of the following provides standards for sterile compounding of pharmaceutical products?

    a. USP Chapter <795>
    b. OSHA
    c. USP Chapter <797>
    d. NIOSH

69. Ten pounds of a drug are required to make 340,000 tablets. How many kilograms of drug are required to make 170,000 tablets?

    a. 2.27
    b. 22.7
    c. 227
    d. 2270

70. The date assigned at the time of preparation after which a compounded product should not be used is referred to as the:

    a. Expiration date
    b. Nonuse date
    c. Compound date
    d. Beyond-use date

71. If a drug contains 50 mg of an expectorant per tablespoon, how many grams would be in a quart of this medication?

    a. 3.2
    b. 9.6
    c. 3200
    d. 9600

72. If an alprazolam tablet contains 0.25 mg of active ingredient, how many grains would be in 50 tablets?

    a. 0.086
    b. 0.192
    c. 0.811
    d. 12.53

73. Use of aseptic technique is important in sterile compounding to:

    a. Avoid drug interactions
    b. Prevent microbial contamination
    c. Decrease costs
    d. Increase quantity of orders filled per day

74. A 2 mL vial of tobramycin sulfate contains 80 mg of the drug. How many milliliters of the injection would be required to obtain 0.02 g of tobramycin sulfate?

a. 0.25
b. 0.5
c. 2.5
d. 5.0

75. An IV set delivers 18 drops for every milliliter. How many drops would be in a 0.5 L bag of intravenous solution?

a. 300
b. 600
c. 9000
d. 18,000

76. If penicillin is mistakenly introduced into a morphine solution after a syringe is reused during the compounding process, which of the following has occurred?

a. Infection
b. Cross-contamination
c. Meningitis
d. Single-source contamination

77. How many milligrams of doxorubicin would be administered in a single dose to a 20-kg 96-cm-tall, 6-year-old child with a body surface area of approximately 0.7 m^2 if the intravenous dose is 30 mg per square meter of body surface area daily on 3 successive days every 4 weeks?

a. 21
b. 30
c. 64
d. 356

78. A patient sends a prescription that reads:

Depakote ER	500 mg
Sig.: 1 tab.	(500 mg) b.i.d.
Dispense:	90 days supply

How many tablets would you dispense?

a. 90
b. 60
c. 360
d. 180

79. How many milliliters of an injection containing 0.5 mg/mL of a drug would provide a 250 mcg dose?

a. 0.2
b. 0.5
c. 2
d. 5

80. How many milligrams of phenytoin would a 46-lb. child receive if the physician wants the child to receive 4 mg of phenytoin per kilogram of body weight?

a. 24
b. 84
c. 184
d. 404

81. A patient presents a prescription that reads:

Metformin	500 mg
Sig.:	2 tab. b.i.d.
Dispense:	90 days supply

How many tablets would you dispense?

a. 240
b. 120
c. 180
d. 360

82. In preparing a pint of elixir containing 200 mcg of an alkaloid per tablespoonful, how many milligrams of the alkaloid would you need to use?

a. 6.4
b. 19.2
c. 6400
d. 19,200

83. The dose of gentamicin is 2.5 mg/kg administered every 12 hours. What would be the daily dose for an 8.8-lb. baby?

a. 10
b. 20
c. 48
d. 96

84. If a drug is required to be stored at room temperature, which of the following temperature ranges would be acceptable for storage?

   a. 52° to 66° F
   b. 64° to 70° F
   c. 68° to 77° F
   d. 78° to 87° F

85. An intravenous solution is ordered to provide a patient 1 L of D5W over 8 hours. How many milliliters per minute would the patient receive?

   a. 2.08
   b. 9.44
   c. 16.62
   d. 125

86. If diphenhydramine elixir contains 12.5 mg diphenhydramine per teaspoonful, how many grams would be required to prepare a quart of the elixir?

   a. 2.4
   b. 800
   c. 1200
   d. 2400

87. Clozapine (Clozaril®):

   a. May cause life-threatening side effects
   b. Is effective in treating severe, disfiguring nodular acne and certain other skin diseases when other therapies have failed
   c. Has been approved by the FDA and is commonly used today
   d. May be dispensed in quantities for a 3-month supply

Use the following information for questions 88–90:

Starch	250 g
Sucrose	150 g
Magnesium sulfate	0.75 g
Lactose	125 g
Yield:	1000 placebo tablets

88. How many kilograms of sucrose would be needed to prepare 50,000 placebo tablets?

   a. 7.5
   b. 12.5
   c. 7500
   d. 12,500

89. How many placebo tablets would contain 5 lb. of starch?

a. 9.08
b. 90.8
c. 908
d. 9080

90. What is the percent of magnesium sulfate in each tablet?

a. 0.00143
b. 0.0143
c. 0.143
d. 1.43

Use the following information for questions 91–95:

The label on a vial directs you to "add 7.8 mL of sterile water" to prepare a 10 mL "multidose" vial of a 100 mg/mL injection.

91. What is the dry powder volume of the drug in this vial?

a. 0.22
b. 2.2
c. 12.2
d. Cannot be determined

92. How many milliliters of reconstituted solution for injection would provide a 300 mg dose?

a. 0.2
b. 0.3
c. 3
d. 20

93. How many grams of the drug are in the vial?

a. 1
b. 10
c. 100
d. 1000

94. If a patient is to receive 250 mg q.i.d. for 10 days, how many multidose vials will be required?

a. 1
b. 10
c. 100
d. 1000

95. How many milliliters of the reconstituted solution would provide a 250 mg dose if the vial was accidentally reconstituted with 9.8 mL of sterile water?

  a. 0.3
  b. 3
  c. 30
  d. Cannot be done

Use the following information for questions 96–99:

A physician orders a patient to receive 4 million units of ampicillin in a 1000 mL bag of an intravenous solution to be infused over 12 hours. The nurse has elected to use an IV set that delivers 15 gtt./mL.

96. How many milliliters of solution will the patient receive per hour?

  a. 0.83
  b. 8.3
  c. 83.3
  d. 830

97. How many units of ampicillin will the patient receive per minute?

  a. 5.55
  b. 55.5
  c. 555
  d. 5555

98. What is the flow rate in milliliters per minute?

  a. 1.39
  b. 13.9
  c. 139
  d. Cannot be determined

99. How many drops per hour will the patient receive?

  a. 1.25
  b. 12.5
  c. 125
  d. 1250

Use the following information for questions 100 and 101:

Precipitated sulfur	5%
Benzocaine	1:500
Zinc oxide paste ad	120 g

100. How many milligrams of benzocaine are contained in this prescription?

a. 0.24
b. 2.4
c. 24
d. 240

101. How many grams of precipitated sulfur would be required to prepare 1 kg of this product?

a. 0.5
b. 5
c. 50
d. 500

102. Cytotoxic drugs:

a. Have all been shown to have an antitestosterone component
b. Are only used to treat breast cancer
c. Do not pose a hazard to health care professionals when properly handled and dispensed
d. Do not require special labeling

103. What is the percent strength of ichthammol in a mixture of 1 kg each of ichthammol ointments containing 10%, 15%, and 20%?

a. 10
b. 15
c. 25
d. 45

Use the following information for questions 104–106:

A fluid ounce of 20% boric acid solution is diluted to 1000 mL with water.

104. What is the percent strength of the dilution?

a. 0.006
b. 0.06
c. 0.6
d. 6

105. What is the ratio strength of the dilution?

   a. 1:2847
   b. 1:1776
   c. 1:345
   d. 1:167

106. How many milligrams of boric acid are in a tablespoonful of the final dilution?

   a. 0.03
   b. 0.09
   c. 30
   d. 90

107. The number of times a product is purchased, sold, and replaced during a specific accounting period is the:

   a. Inventory control period
   b. Inventory turnover rate
   c. Inventory management rate
   d. Inventory level

Use the following information for questions 108–111:

A 95% alcohol solution is mixed with 45% alcohol solution to make a 55% solution.

108. In what proportions should the alcohols be mixed to prepare the 55% solution?

   a. 40 parts 95% and 10 parts 45%
   b. 30 parts 95% and 20 parts 45%
   c. 20 parts 95% and 30 parts 45%
   d. 10 parts 95% and 40 parts 45%

109. How many milliliters of the 95% alcohol solution are required to prepare a liter of the 55% solution?

   a. 100
   b. 200
   c. 400
   d. 800

110. How many milliliters of the 45% alcohol solution are required to prepare a liter of the 55% solution?

   a. 100
   b. 200
   c. 400
   d. 800

111. How many milliliters of the 55% mixture can be prepared by mixing 45% and 95% alcohol solutions if you have only a pint of 95% alcohol and 3 gal. of 45% alcohol?

   a. 1200
   b. 2400
   c. 4300
   d. 8800

112. Accutane®:

   a. Is commonly used to treat cancer in patients from 16 to 45 years old
   b. Effectively treats disfiguring nodular acne
   c. Effectively treats actinic onychomycosis on a limited basis
   d. Causes a severe interaction when patient is also taking isotretinoin

Use the following information for questions 113–116:

A pharmacist purchases a box containing a dozen tubes of zinc oxide for $14.88 and sells the tubes of ointment for $2.69 each.

113. What is the markup on each tube?

   a. $0.88
   b. $1.25
   c. $1.45
   d. $2.48

114. What is the percent markup based on selling price?

   a. 22%
   b. 48%
   c. 54%
   d. 117%

115. What is the percent markup based on cost?

   a. 22%
   b. 48%
   c. 54%
   d. 117%

116. What would a tube cost if the store offered a 30% discount on all topical products?

   a. $0.65
   b. $1.16
   c. $1.88
   d. $3.49

117. Which drug is commonly used to treat diabetes?

a. Gabapentin
b. Sular
c. Metformin
d. Sotalol

118. Amitriptyline is used to treat:

a. High blood pressure
b. Depression
c. Diabetes
d. None of the above

119. Simvastatin is the generic name for:

a. Lipitor®
b. Tricor®
c. Advicor®
d. Zocor®

120. A prescription is written for amoxicillin 500 mg, take 2 capsules (1000 mg) daily. What is the strength of amoxicillin in this prescription?

a. 500 mg
b. 1000 mg
c. 1500 mg
d. 2000 mg

Use the following information for questions 121–125:

A liter bottle of an enteral feeding formulation contains the following:

1200 calories	1200 mg sodium
2000 mg potassium	43 g protein
170 g carbohydrates	10 g fiber
39 g fat	

121. How many calories would a patient receive from 1500 mL of this formulation?

a. 600
b. 1200
c. 1800
d. 2400

122. Approximately how many milligrams of protein would a patient receive in an hour if the administration rate is 60 mL/hr.?

a. 2.6
b. 26
c. 260
d. 2600

123. How many total kilograms of fat and carbohydrates would a patient receive from 2 bottles of this formulation?

a. 0.418
b. 4.18
c. 41.8
d. 418

124. What would be the administration rate in milliliters per hour of the formulation if a physician wants the patient to receive 160 mg potassium every hour?

a. 8
b. 40
c. 60
d. 80

125. How many micrograms of fiber would be in a tablespoonful of this formulation?

a. 0.15
b. 1.5
c. 150
d. 150,000

The **Answer Key** appears in **Section VIII**.

Notes:

Answer Key

Chapter 1

1. a
2. b
3. d
4. a
5. c
6. a
7. c

Chapter 2

1. d
2. a
3. d
4. b
5. c
6. a
7. b
8. c

Chapter 3

1. c
2. a
3. b
4. a
5. a
6. d
7. c
8. b
9. c

Chapter 4

1. a
2. c
3. d
4. d
5. b
6. c
7. a

Chapter 5

1. d
2. a
3. b
4. c
5. a
6. b
7. d

Chapter 6

1. c
2. a
3. d
4. b
5. d
6. a
7. c
8. a
9. d
10. d

Chapter 7

1. b
2. a
3. a
4. c
5. d
6. d
7. a
8. d

Chapter 8

1. a
2. d
3. b
4. d
5. c
6. d

Chapter 9

1. a
2. b
3. c
4. c
5. a
6. d
7. d

Chapter 10

1. c
2. a
3. b
4. d
5. b
6. d
7. c
8. c
9. b
10. a

Chapter 11

1. b
2. c
3. c
4. d
5. a

Chapter 12

1. b
2. a
3. d
4. c

Chapter 13

1. b
2. a
3. d
4. b
5. d
6. c
7. b
8. c
9. a
10. b

Chapter 14

1a. $\frac{10 \div 5}{75 \div 5} = \frac{2}{15}$

1b. $\frac{8 \div 8}{16 \div 8} = \frac{1}{2}$

1c. $\frac{3 \div 3}{15 \div 3} = \frac{1}{5}$

1d. 60/186 = 30/93 = 10/31

2a. 5 = 5/1

2b. 3 2/3 = 11/3

3a. 30/64, 12/64, 7/64

3b. 18/24, 21/24, 10/24

4. 15/4 = 3 3/4

5. 3/4 + 1 1/8 = 6/8 + 9/8 = 15/8 = 1 7/8

6. 7 5/8 – 1 1/3 = 61/8 – 4/3 = 183/24 – 32/24 = 151/24 = 6 7/24

7. 1 3/4 × 3 = 7/4 × 3/1 = 21/4 = 5 1/4

8. 1/2 ÷ 5 = 1/2 ÷ 5/1 = 1/2 × 1/5 = 1/10

9. 3/16 ÷ 1 1/2 = 3/16 ÷ 3/2 = 3/16 × 2/3 = 6/48 = 1/8

10a. 0.07 = 7/100

10b. 0.077 = 77/1000

10c. 5.0125 = 5 125/10,000 = 5 1/80

11a. 3/8 = 0.375

11b. 2 7/13 = 33/13 = 2.54

12a. 3.75 – 1/2 = 3.75 – 0.5 = 3.25

12b. 3/4 × 2.5 = 0.75 × 2.5 = 1.875

12c. 2 3/8 ÷ 0.5 = 2.375 ÷ 0.5 = 4.75

13a. 29 = XXIX

13b. 47 = XLVII

13c. 86 = LXXXVI

13d. 1154 = MCLIV

14a. LXXVIII = 78

14b. CXIII = 113

14c. XCIV = 94

14d. MCMLXI = 1961

15. 3/8 = 0.375
0.375 ÷ 0.0125 = 30 doses

16. Step 1: 2 × 1.25 = 2.5
3 × 1.75 = 5.25
———————
7.75 oz. dispensed
Step 2: 8 – 7.75 = 0.25 oz. remaining in the bottle

17. 1/200 ÷ 1/40 = 1/200 × 40/1 = 40/200 = 1/5 tablet

18. 1/150 ÷ 1/400 = 1/150 × 400/1 = 400/150 = 2 2/3 tablets

19. 10 × 44 = 440 = CDXL

20. 9 + 6 + 60 = 75 g

21. 515 – 66 = 449 lb.

22. 20 × 445 = 8900 mg

23. 251 × 4 = 1004 = MIV

24. 120 × 4 = 480 = CDLXXX

25a. 3/1 × 3/8 = 9/8 = 1 1/8 lb.

25b. 1 1/8 = 9/8 = 18/16
18/16 – 3/16 = 15/16 lb.

26. 1/150 × 4 = 4/150 = 0.0267 gr.

27a. 120 mL/24 tsp. = 5 mL/1 tsp.

27b. 24 tsp./0.75 tsp. = 32 doses

28. 24 × 325 = 7800 mg

29a. 100 × 9/8 = 900/8 = 112.5 g

29b. 200 – 112.5 = 87.5 g

30. 1635/109 = 15 technicians

31. 0.75/0.004 = 187.5 doses

Chapter 15

1a. 72% = 72/100 = 0.72

1b. 0.35 = 35% = 35/100 = 7/20

1c. 25% = 25/100 = 25:100

1d. 0.182 = 18.2%

1e. 3/8 = 0.375 = 37.5%

2a. $40

A/B = C/D

10 lb./$200 = 2 lb./x

(x) (10 lb.) = ($200) (2 lb.)

x = ($200) (2 lb.) / 10 lb.

x = $40

2b. 1.25 lb.

A/B = C/D

10 lb./$200 = x/$25

($25) (10 lb.) = ($200) (x)

($25) (10 lb.) / ($200) = x

x = 1.25 lb.

2c. $12.50

Step 1: A/B = C/D

1 lb./16 oz. = 10 lb./x

(10 lb.) (16 oz.) / 1 lb. = x

x = 160 oz. (160 oz. cost $200 as mentioned earlier)

Step 2: A/B = C/D

160 oz./$200 = 10 oz./x

(10 oz.) ($200) = (160 oz.) (x)

(10 oz.) ($200) / 160 oz. = x

x = $12.50

3. 5.46 g

1000 tab./11.5 g = 475 tab./x

x = 5.46 g

4. 160 mg

5 mg/15 mL = x/480 mL

x = 160 mg

5. 32,500 mg

2 tab./650 mg = 100 tab./x

x = 32,500 mg

6. 300 tablets

7 tab./35 mg = x/1500 mg

x = 300 tablets

7. $52.20

$0.58/1 tab. = x/90 tab.

x = $52.20

8. 0.65 g

1 cap./0.0325 g = 20 cap./x

x = 0.65 g

9. $206.49

385 lb./$795 = 100 lb./x

x = $206.49

10. 78.64 kg

2.2 lb./1 kg = 173 lb./x

x = 78.64 kg

11. 300,000 units

6,000,000 units/10 mL = x/0.5 mL

x = 300,000 units

12. 300 mL

5 mL/1 min. = x/60 min.

x = 300 mL

13. 5250 mg

750 mg/1 day = x/7 days

x = 5250 mg

14. 11.2 mg

28 mg/3 mL = x/1.2 mL

x = 11.2 mg

15. 1.5 g
    10 g/100 mL = x/15 mL
    x = 1.5 g
16. $8.96
    15 mL/$0.28 = 480 mL/x
    x = $8.96
17a. $1.35
    12 bottles/$1.80 = 9 bottles/x
    x = $1.35
17b. $18.00
    1 dozen/$1.80 = 10 dozen/x
    x = $18.00
18a. 4.5 min.
    60 sec./1 min. = 270 sec./x
    x = 4.5 min.
18b. 100 Rx
    7.5 hr. × 60 min./hr. = 450 min.
    1 Rx/4.5 min. = x/450 min.
    x = 100 Rx
19a. 90 tablets
    3 tab./day = x/30 days
    x = 90 tablets
19b. 450 mg
    5 mg/1 tab. = x/90 tab.
    x = 450 mg
20a. 4.54/454 = 0.01
20b. 0.01 = 1/100 = 1%
21. 20/100 = 2/10 = 1/5 = 1:5
22a. $3.67
    6 oz./$88 = 1/4/x
    x = $3.67
22b. 0.068 oz.
    6 oz./$88 = x/$1
    x = 0.068 oz.
23a. 3/16 g
    100/3/8 = 50/x
    x = 3/16 g
23b. 3/16 = 0.1875 = 18.75%

Chapter 16

1a. 225 km = 225,000 m
    1 km/1000 m = 225 km/x
1b. 525 g = 0.525 kg
    1 kg/1000 g = x/525 g
1c. 5 g = 5000 mg
    1 g/1000 mg = 5 g/x
    5 g = 5,000,000 mcg
    1 g/1,000,000 mcg = 5 g/x
1d. 350 mL = 0.35 L
    1 L/1000 mL = x/350 mL
2a. 480 mL
    30 mL/1 oz. = x/16 oz.
2b. 32 fluid oz.
    1 pt./16 fluid oz. = 2 pt./x
2c. 8 pints
    2 pt./1 qt. = x/4 qt.
    128 fluid ounces
    16 oz./1 pt. = x/8 pt.
3a. 7000 gr.
    1 oz./437.5 gr. = 16 oz./x
3b. 7.62 cm
    1 inch/2.54 cm = 3 inches/x
4a. 0.065 g
    1 g/15.4 gr. = x/1 gr.
    65 mg
    1 g/1000 mg = 0.065 g/x
4b. 437.5 gr.
    28.4 g
    1 g/15.4 gr. = x/437.5 gr.
4c. 16 oz.
    454 g
    1 oz./28.4 g = 16 oz./x
    7000 gr.
    1 g/15.4 gr. = 454 g/x
    0.454 kg
    1 kg/1000 g = x/454 g

4d. 2.2 lb.
454 g/1 lb. = 1000 g/x

5a. 16 fluid oz.
480 mL
1 oz./30 mL = 16 oz./x

5b. 128 fluid oz.
16 oz./1 pt. = x/8 pt.
3840 mL
1 oz./30 mL = 128 oz./x
3.84 L
1 L/1000 mL = x/3840 mL

6. 68°F
°F = 32 + 9/5 °C
°F = 32 + 9/5 (20)
°F = 32 + 36
°F = 68°

7. 100°C
°C = 5/9 (°F – 32)
°C = 5/9 (212 – 32)
°C = 5/9 (180)
°C = 100

8. 1538 tablets
Step 1: 0.5 kg = 500 g = 500,000 mg
Step 2: 325 mg/1 tab. = 500,000 mg/x
x = 1538 tablets

9. 111.8 kg
2.2 lb./1 kg = 246 lb./x
x = 111.8 kg

10. 8000 mcg
Step 1: 40 mg = 40,000 mcg
Step 2: 40,000 mcg/10 mL = x/2 mL
x = 8000 mcg

11. 38.5 gr.
Step 1: 10 g/1000 mL = x/250 mL
x = 2.5 g
Step 2: 1 g/15.4 gr. = 2.5 g/x
x = 38.5 gr.

12a. 28.8 oz.
16 oz./1 lb. = x/1.8 lb.
x = 28.8 oz.

12b. $252
1 oz./$8.75 = 28.8 oz./x
x = $252

12c. $6.56
1 oz./$8.75 = 3/4 oz./x
x = $6.56

13a. 96 bottles
4 oz./1 bottle = 384 oz./x
x = 96 bottles

13b. $1.25
128 oz./$40 = 4 oz./x
x = $1.25

14a. 800,000 x 15 = 12,000,000 mg =
12,000 g = 12 kg

14b. 26.43 lb.
454 g/1 lb. = 12,000 g/x
x = 26.43 lb.

14c. 423 oz.
1 lb./16 oz. = 26.43 lb./x
x = 423 oz.

14d. $6281
1 oz./$14.85 = 423 oz./x
x = $6281

15a. 84 kg
2.2 lb./kg = 185 lb./x
x = 84 kg

15b. 252 mg
3 mg/kg = x/84 kg
x = 252 mg

16. °C = 5/9 (°F – 32) = 5/9 (–90) = –50

17. °F = 32 + 9/5 °C = 32 + (–27) = 5

Chapter 17

1a. 3 tsp.
1 tsp./5 mL = x/15 mL

1b. 6 tsp.
1 tsp./5 mL = x/30 mL
2 tbsp.
1 tbsp./15 mL = x/30 mL

1c. 16 fluid oz.
480 mL
1 fluid oz./30 mL = 16 fluid oz./x
32 tbsp.
1 tbsp./15 mL = x/480 mL
96 tsp.
1 tbsp./3 tsp. = 32 tbsp./x
or
1 tsp./5 mL = x/480 mL

2a. 2.2 lb.
454 g/1 lb. = 1000 g/x

2b. 0.4 g
20 mg/2.2 lb. = x/44 lb.
x = 400 mg = 0.4 g

2c. 133 mg
400 mg/3 doses = 133 mg/1 dose

2d. approximately 1 tsp.
125 mg/1 tsp. = 133 mg/x
x = 1.064 tsp.

2e. approximately 3 tsp.
125 mg/1 tsp. = 400 mg/x
x = 3.2 tsp.

2f. 150 mL
15 mL/1 day = x/10 days

2g. 5 fluid oz.
1 fluid oz./30 mL = x/150 mL

2h. 21 doses
3 doses/1 day = x/7 days

3. 180 mL
Step 1: 15 mL/1 dose = x/4 doses
x = 60 mL/day
Step 2: 60 mL/1 day = x/3 days
x = 180 mL

4a. 600 mL
Step 1: 30 drops/1 min. = x/360 min.
x = 10,800 drops
Step 2: 18 drops/1 mL = 10,800 drops/x
x = 600 mL

4b. 5.4 g
0.9 g NaCl/100 mL = x/600 mL

5a. 4.3 minutes
Step 1: 1 kg/2.2 lb.= 90 kg/x
x = 198 lb.
Step 2: 1 mcg/1 lb. = x/198 lb.
x = 198 mcg = 0.198 mg/min.
Step 3: 0.198 mg/1 min. = 0.85 mg/x
x = 4.3 minutes

5b. 0.5 mL/min.
2 mg/5 mL = 0.198 mg/x
x = 0.5 mL/min.

5c. 2.15 mL
0.5 mL/1 min. = x/4.3 min.
or
2 mg/5 mL = 0.85 mg/x
x = 2.13 mL

6. 3.33 mL
Step 1: 6 mg/lb. = x/50 lb.
x = 300 mg
Step 2: 90 mg/1 mL = 300 mg/x
x = 3.33 mL

7. 120 tablets
   Step 1: 5 mg/lb. = x/100 lb.
   x = 500 mg daily
   Step 2: 125 mg/tab. = 500 mg/x
   x = 4 tablets daily
   Step 3: 4 tab./day = x/30 days
   x = 120 tablets

8. 2.4 mL
   Step 1: 1 kg/2.2 lb. = x/66 lb.
   x = 30 kg patient's weight
   Step 2: 10 mg/1 kg = x/30 kg
   x = 300 mg
   Step 3: 125 mg/1 mL = 300 mg/x
   x = 2.4 mL

9. 0.4 mL
   Step 1: 100 mcg = 0.1 mg
   Step 2: 0.5 mg/2 mL = 0.1 mg/x
   x = 0.4 mL

10. 0.59 mg
   Step 1: 28 gtt./1 mL = 15 gtt./x
   x = 0.54 mL
   Step 2: 1.1 mg/1 mL = x/0.54 mL
   x = 0.59 mg

11. 0.21 g
   30 mg/1 day = x/7 days
   x = 210 mg = 0.21 g

12a. 36 tsp. doses
   1 tsp./5 mL = x/180 mL
   x = 36 tsp. doses

12b. 6 days
   1 dose/4 hr. = 36 doses/x
   x = 144 hours = 6 days

13. 5 mL
   50 mcg/mL = 250 mcg/x
   x = 5 mL

14a. 40 capsules
   1 × 4 × 10 = 40 capsules

14b. $0.42
   40 cap./$16.80 = 1 cap./x
   x = $0.42

15a. 150 mL
   5 mL × 3 × 10 = 150 mL

15b. 10 days
   7.5 × 2 = 15 mL/day
   150 mL/15 mL = 10 days

16a. 36 mg
   3 mg/1 lb. = x/12 lb.
   x = 36 mg

16b. 4.5 mL
   8 mg/1 mL = 36 mg/x
   x = 4.5 mL

17a. 32 doses
   1 dose/15 mL = x/480 mL
   x = 32 doses

17b. 1.5 g
   10 g/100 mL = x/15 mL
   x = 1.5 g

17c. 48,000 mg
   10 g/100 mL = x/480 mL
   x = 48 g = 48,000 mg

18a. 125 mL
   1000 mL/8 hr. = x/1 hr.
   x = 125 mL

18b. 21 gtt./min.
   125 mL/60 min. = x/1 min.
   x = 2.08 mL/min.
   10 gtt./1 mL = x/2.08 mL
   x = 21 gtt./min.

19a. 1.8 m^2
   Use adult nomogram to get 1.8 m^2

19b. 0.72 mg
   0.4 mg/1 m^2 *= x/1.8* m^2
   x = 0.72 mg

Chapter 18

1a. 19.2 g or 19,200 mg

5 g triet./1000 mL = x/3840 mL

x = 19.2 g = 19,200 mg

1 g/1000 mg = 19.2 g/x

1b. 148 gr.

Step 1: 20 g/1000 mL = x/480 mL

x = 9.6 g

Step 2: 1 g/15.4 gr. = 9.6 g/x

x = 148 gr.

1c. 5 tsp.

Step 1: 250 mL B.B./1000 mL lotion

= x/100 mL lotion

x = 25 mL B.B.

Step 2: 1 tsp./5 mL = x/25 mL

x = 5 tsp.

2a. 1.67%

2 g/120 g = 0.0167 = 1.67%

2b. 16.7 mg

2 g sulfur/120 g ung. = x/1 g ung.

x = 0.0167 g = 16.7 mg

3. 4.4%

20 g/454 g = 0.044 = 4.4%

4a. 29.4%

50 g/(50 g + 120 g) = 0.294 = 29.4%

Note: The 50 g sulfur was added to 120 g petrolatum, so the final product weighed 170 g.

4b. 70.6%

120 g pet./170 g ung. = 0.706 = 70.6%

Note: One could also take previous answer and subtract from 100% (i.e., 100% – 29.4% = 70.6%).

5. 22.5 g ZnO

0.25 × 90 g = 22.5 g

6a. 6.25%

30 mL/480 mL = 0.0625 = 6.25%

6b. 3.75 mL

30 mL/480 mL = x/60 mL

or

0.0625 × 60 = 3.75 mL

7. 4.67%

7 g/150 mL = 0.0467 = 4.67%

8a. 11.8%

454 g/3840 mL = 0.118 = 11.8%

8b. 1:8.46

454 g/3840 mL = 1/x

x = 8.46

Note: The ratio is 1/8.46 or 1:8.46.

9a. 48 g

0.10 × 480 = 48

9b. 10%

Note: Percent is the same for any volume of a percent solution.

10. 2%

1:50 = 1/50 = 0.02 = 2%

19.2 g

0.02 × 960 mL = 19.2 g

11a. 60 mg

Step 1: 6% means 6 g/100 mL or 6000 mg/100 mL

Step 2: 6000 mg/100 mL = x/1 mL

11b. 1:16.67

6% = 6 g/100 mL

6 g/100 mL = 1/x

x = 16.67

Note: The ratio is 1/16.67 or 1:16.67.

12. 0.83%

Step 1: 2000 mg = 2 g and

8 fluid oz. = 240 mL

Step 2: 2 g/240 mL = 0.0083 = 0.83%

1:120

2 g/240 mL = 1/x

x = 120; ratio is 1:120

8.33 mg

2000 mg/240 mL = x/1 mL

13a. 1:120

6/720 = 1/x x = 120

so 6:720 equals 1:120

13b. 0.833%

6/720 = 0.00833 = 0.833%

14a. 1.063%

(30 mL) (17%) = (480 mL) (x)

14b. 1:94

1.063/100 = 1/x x = 94

14c. 10.63 mg

Step 1: 1.063 g/100 mL =

1063 mg/100 mL

Step 2: 1063 mg/100 mL = x/1 mL

x = 10.63 mg

14d. 0.85 g

0.17 × 5 mL = 0.85

14e. 4.25%

(5 mL) (17%) = (20 mL) (x)

x = 4.25%

Note: The final solution is 20 mL

(5 mL added to 15 mL).

14f. 78.54 gr.

Step 1: 0.17 × 30 = 5.1 g

Step 2: 1 g/15.4 gr. = 5.1 g/x

x = 78.54 gr.

14g. 78.54 gr.

Note: The benzalkonium chloride in the initial 30 mL is all that will be in the final 480 mL. The 30 mL was diluted with a diluent that does not contain any additional benzalkonium chloride.

14h. 1:2000

(100 mL) (0.5%) = (1000 mL) (x)

x = 0.05% = 0.0005 = 5/10,000 =

5:10,000 = 1:2000

14i. 2.5 mg

Step 1: 5 g/10,000 mL

5000 mg/10,000 mL

Step 2: 5000 mg/10,000 mL = x/5 mL

or

0.0005 (5 mL) = 0.0025 g = 2.5 mg

15a. yes

(10% is between 5% and 20%)

15b. 151 g of 20%

Alligation Alternate Method

Note: The total amount made of 10% is the sum of the parts:

5 parts + 10 parts = 15 parts

In this case, it is 454 g, so

$$\frac{15 \text{ parts}}{454 \text{ g}} = \frac{5 \text{ parts}}{x}$$

303 g of 5%

15 parts/454 = 10 parts/x

or 454 g (total) – 151 g (of 20%) = 303 g of 5%

15c. 90 g of 10%

5 parts/30 g = 15 parts/x x = 90 g

16a. no

(10% is not between 20% and 15%)

16b. not possible

16c. not possible

17. 9 g NaCl

0.009 × 1000 mL = 9 g

153.8 mEq Na^+

58.5 mg/L mEq = 9000 mg/x

Note: MW of NaCl = 58.5.

18a. 0.745%

Step 1: MW KCl = 74.5 mg = 1 mEq

Step 2: 10 mEq = 745 mg = 0.745 g

Step 3: 0.745 g/100 mL =

0.00745 = 0.745%

18b. 7450 mg

Step 1: 10 mEq/100 mL =

x/1000 mL

x = 100 mEq

Step 2: 1 mEq KCl/74.5 mg

KCl = 100 mEq KCl/x

x = 7450 mg

19. 4.5 mEq

Step 1: mEq CaCl2 = 111/2 = 55.5 mg

Step 2: 55.5 mg/1 mEq = 250 mg/x

20. 1.67%

Step 1: 250 mg = 0.25 g

Step 2: 0.25 g/15 mL =

0.0167 = 1.67%

21. 38.5 mEq

Step 1: MW of $Al(OH)_3$ *= 78*

Step 2: 1 mEq = 78/3 = 26 mg

Step 3: 1 mEq $Al(OH)_3$*/26 mg =*

x/1000 mg

x = 38.5 mEq

22a. 200 mL

5 mL/dose × 4 doses/day ×

10 days = 200 mL

22b. 40 mL

200 mL – 160 mL H_2O *= 40 mL*

22c. 7 g

250 mg x 4 doses/day = 1000 mg = 1 g/day

1 g/1 day = x/7 days

x = 7 g

23. 8.33 tablets

Step 1: 1 cap./5 mg codeine = 50 cap./x

x = 250 mg

Step 2: 30 mg/1 tab. = 250 mg/x

x = 8.33 tablets

24a. 12 tablets

Step 1: (0.02 × 150) = 3 g = 3000 mg

Step 2: 250 mg/1 tab. = 3000 mg/x

x = 12 tablets

24b. 1:50

Note: 1 tsp. of 2% is still 2%, so 2% = 0.02

= 2/100 = 2:100 = 1:50

24c. 20 mg

Step 1: 2% × 150 = 3 g = 3000 mg

Step 2: 3000 mg/150 mL = x/1 mL

x = 20 mg

25a. 7500 mg

500 mg/1 mL = x/15

x = 7500 mg

25b. no

25c. yes

25d. 2.2 mL

15 mL (final volume) – 12.8 mL

(diluent) = 2.2 mL (powder volume displacement)

25e. 4 mL

500 mg/1 mL = 2000 mg/x

x = 4 mL

25f. 3.25 mL

10 mL (diluent) + 2.2 mL (powder

volume displacement) = 12.2 mL

(final volume containing 7500 mg of the drug)

7500 mg/12.2 mL = 2000 mg/x

x = 3.25 mL

26a. 8.25%

Alligation Medial Method

0.5 kg × 3% = 1.5 kg%

1.5 kg × 10% = 15.0 kg%

---

2 kg 16.5 kg%

16.5kg%/2 kg = 8.25%

26b. 1:12.12

8.25/100 = 1/x

x = 12.12

26c. 37.5 g

454 × 8.25% = 37.5 g

26d. no

26e. 237.8 g

Step 1: Alligation Alternate Method

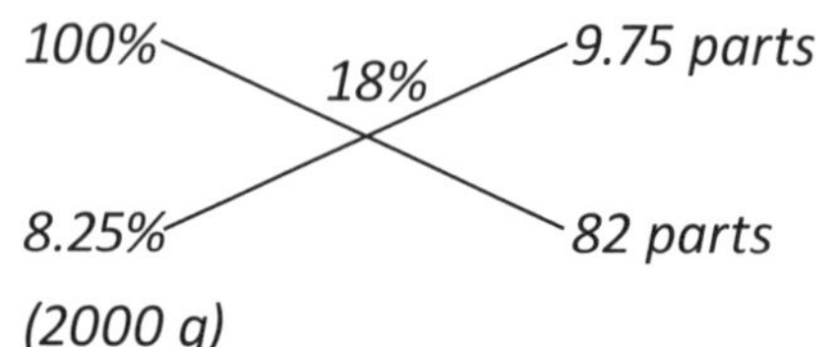

(2000 g)

Step 2: 82 parts/2000 g =

9.75 parts/x

x = 237.8 g

Chapter 19

1a. $20

1 cap./$0.20 = 100 cap./x

x = $20

1b. $0.25 each

$0.20 cost plus $0.05 profit

1c. $7.50

1 cap./$0.25 = 30 cap./x

x = $7.50

2a. $10

Selling Price = Cost + Markup

$60 = $50 + Markup

Markup = $60 – $50 = $10

2b. 20%

Markup/Cost = $10/$50 = 0.2 = 20%

2c. 16.7%

Markup/Selling price = $10/$60 = 0.167 = 16.7%

3a. $20

$65 – $45 = $20 Markup

3b. 31%

$20/$65 = 0.31 = 31%

3c. 44%

$20/$45 = 0.44 = 44%

3d. $77.40

1.72 × $45 = $77.40

4a. $55

$65 – $10 = $55

4b. $1.63

40 cap./$65 = 1 cap./x

x = $1.63/cap.

4c. $0.25

$10 Markup/40 cap. = x/1 cap.

x = $0.25

4d. $22.75

40 cap./$65 = 14 cap./x

x = $22.75

4e. 18%

$10/$55 = 0.18 = 18%

4f. 15.4%

$10/$65 = 0.154 = 15.4%

Chapter 20

1. c
2. d

   1 g/30,000 mL = x/3000 mL

   x = 0.1 g = 100 mg
3. b

   Step 1: 250 units/1 g = x/1000 g

   x = 250,000 units

   Step 2: 500 units/1 g =

   250,000 units/x x = 500 g
4. c
5. a

   Step 1: 10,000 mcg = 10 mg = 0.01 g

   Step 2: 0.1 g/10 mL = 0.01 g/x

   x = 1 mL
6. d

   1/4% = 0.25%

   0.25% × 30 = 0.0025 × 30 =

   0.075 g = 75 mg
7. c
8. c

   Step 1: 30 mEq/1000 mL = 5 mEq/x

   x = 167 mL

   Step 2: 167 mL/60 min. = x/1 min.

   x = 2.78 mL/min.

   Step 3: 15 gtt./1 mL = x/2.78 mL

   x = 41.7 or 42 gtt./min
9. a

   0.9 g/100 mL = 60 g/x

   x = 6666 mL = 6.67 L
10. d

   Step 1: Alligation Alternate Method

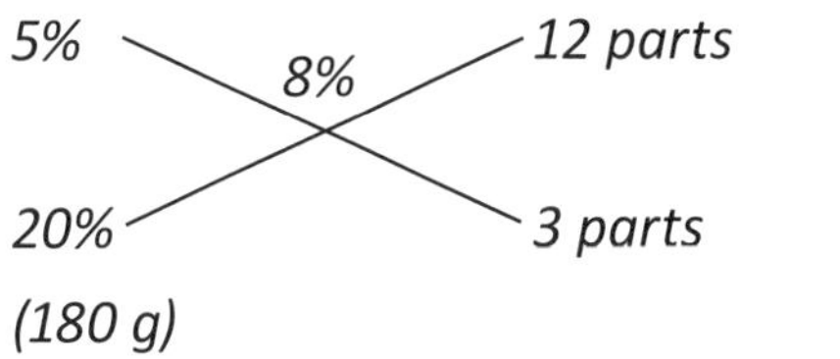

   (180 g)

   Step 2: 3 parts/180 g = 12 parts/x

   x = 720 g
11. b

   2000 mg/5.8 mL = x/1 mL

   x = 345 mg
12. d
13. b
14. a

   Step 1: 2.2 lb./1 kg = 220 lb./x

   x = 100 kg

   Step 2: 5 mcg/1 kg = x/100 kg

   x = 500 mcg = 0.5 mg/min.

   Step 3: 0.5 mg/1 min = x/60 min.

   x = 30 mg per hour

   Step 4: 800 mg/500 mL = 30 mg/x

   x = 18.75 mL

   Note: Sometimes µg is used to represent micrograms or mcg. However, the preferred abbreviation for micrograms is mcg.
15. c

   Step 1: 2.2 lb./1 kg = 264 lb./x

   x = 120 kg

   Step 2: 10 mg/1 kg = x/120 kg

   x = 1200 mg

   Step 3: 200 mg/1 tab. = 1200 mg/x

   x = 6 tab.
16. c

   1 g/750 mL = x/960 mL

   x = 1.28 g
17. c

18. a

Step 1: total weight of recipe:
400 + 150 + 100 + 350 = 1000 g
Step 2: 400 g glycerin/1000 g zinc gel = x/454 g zinc gel
x = 181.6 g

19. d

20. b

Step 1: 1/2 pt. = 240 mL
Step 2: 2 gal. = 7680 mL
Step 3: 1 bottle/240 mL = x/7680 mL
x = 32 bottles

21. b

22. b

Step 1: Alligation Medial Method

90 mL × 14%	*= 1260 mL%*
100 mL × 0%	*= 0*
40 mL × 78%	*= 3120 mL%*
230 mL	*4380 mL%*

Step 2: 4380 mL%/230 mL = 19.04%

23. c

24. c

Step 1: 2.2 lb./1 kg = 38 lb./x
x = 17.27 kg
Step 2: 35 mg/1 kg = x/17.27 kg
x = 604.54 mg (total daily dose)
Step 3: 604.54 mg/6 doses = x/1 dose
x = 100.8 mg per dose

25. d

0.5 mg/2 mL = x/0.75 mL
x = 0.1875 mg = 187.5 mcg

26. a

27. a

Step 1: 1 mEq = 74.5 mg/L (valence) = 74.5 mg
Step 2: 74.5 mg/1 mEq = x/3 mEq
x = 223.5 mg
Step 3: 223.5 mg/5 mL = x/1000 mL
x = 44,700 mg = 44.7 g

28. a

(old vol.) (old %) = (new vol.)(new %)
(O.V.) (O.%) = (N.V.)(N.%)
(x) (20%) = (600 mL) (0.5%)
x = 15 mL

29. b

30. b

Step 1: Alligation Alternate Method

1% (30 g) — *95 parts*
5%
100% — *4 parts*

Step 2: 95 parts/30 g = 4 parts/x
x = 1.26 g

31. c

500 mcg/15 mL = x/1000 mL
x = 33,333 mcg = 33.33 mg

32. c

3 g/$24.50 = 0.5 g/x
x = $4.08

33. d

Step 1: 500 mg/1 dose = x/4 doses
x = 2000 mg/day
Step 2: 2000 mg/1 day = x/10 days
x = 20,000 mg for 10 days
Step 3: 250 mg/5 mL = 20,000 mg/x
x = 400 mL

34. c

35. d

36. d

Step 1: Alligation Alternate Method

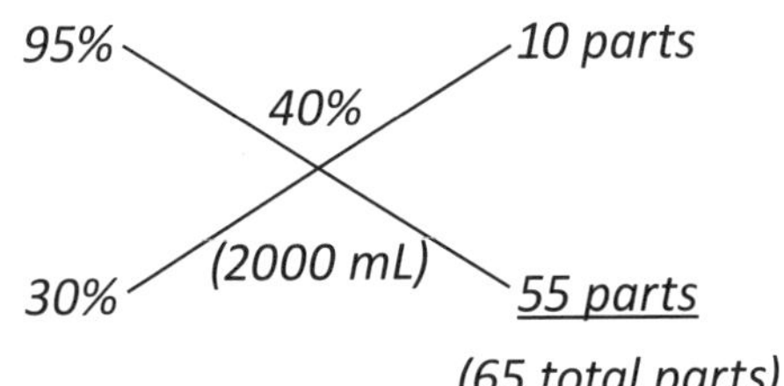

Step 2: 65 parts/2000 mL = 10 parts/x

x = 308 mL

37. a

Step 1: 4 × 480 mL = 1920 mL

Step 2: 1 g/1000 mL = x/1920 mL

x = 1.92 g

38. b

Step 1: 1 mEq potassium gluconate = MW/valence = 234/1 = 234 mg

Step 2: 2 tbsp. = 30 mL

Step 3: 30 mL × 30% = 9 g (i.e., 30 mL × 0.3 = 9 g)

Step 4: 9 g = 9000 mg

Step 5: 1 mEq potassium gluconate/ 234 mg = x/9000 mg

x = 38.46 mEq

39. b

180 mg/5 mL = 280 mg/x

x = 7.78 mL

40. c

41. b

42. d

Step 1: Alligation Alternate Method

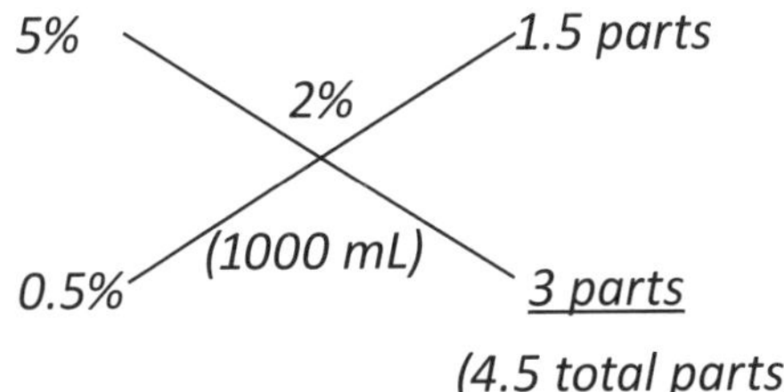

Step 2: 4.5 parts/1000 mL = 3 parts/x

x = 667 mL

43. b

Step 1: 18 g/1000 mL = x/5 mL

x = 0.09 g = 90 mg

Step 2: 65 mg/1 gr. = 90 mg/x

x = 1.38 gr.

44. c

Step 1: 1 g/15.4 gr. = 28 g/x

x = 431.2 gr.

Step 2: 1 3/8 gr./1 cap. = 431.2 gr./x

x = 313 capsules

45. b

$8.75/120 mL = x/15 mL

x = $1.09

46. a

Step 1: 1 mEq = MW/valence = 389/1 = 389 mg

Step 2: 1 mEq K. pcn. V/389 mg = x/2000 mg

x = 5.14 mEq

47. a

Step 1: 1200 mg/60 min. = x/1 min.

x = 20 mg/min.

Step 2: 50 mg/1 mL = 20 mg/x

x = 0.4 mL

48. b

Step 1: 2.2 lb./1 kg = 5.5 lb./x

x = 2.5 kg (infant's weight)

Step 2: 2.5 mg gentamicin/ 1 kg = x/2.5 kg

x = 6.25 mg (dose)

Step 3: 20 mg gentamicin/1 mL = 6.25 mg gentamicin/x

x = 0.31 mL

49. c

Step 1: 1 mEq calcium =
AW/valence = 40/2 = 20 mg
Step 2: 1 mEq/20 mg = 5 mEq/x
x = 100 mg
Step 3: 100 mg/50 mL = x/1000 mL
x = 2000 mg/L

50. d

2% × 60 g = 1.2 g = 1200 mg
benzocaine
(i.e., 0.02 x 60 = 1.2)

51. d

Step 1: 400 gr. × 3/8 = 150 gr.
Step 2: 437.5 gr. – 150 gr. = 287.5 gr.

52. a

53. d

1000 mg/4.1 mL = 675 mg/x
x = 2.77 mL

54. c

Step 1: From problem #53 the dry powder
displacement is 0.7 mL
4.1 – 3.4 = 0.7 mL
Step 2: For problem #54
4.3 mL + 0.7 mL = 5 mL
(new and incorrect volume)
Step 3: Note: The 5 mL contains 1 g of nafcillin
1000 mg/5 mL = 675 mg/x
x = 3.375 = 3.4 mL

55. b

Step 1: 0.1% = 0.1 g/100 mL =
100 mg/100 mL
Step 2: 100 mg/100 mL = 75 mg/x
x = 75 mL

56. c

°F = 32 + 9/5 °C
°F = 32 + (9/5 × 65)
°F = 32 + 117
°F = 149

57. b

58. d

Step 1: 50% = 50 g/100 mL
Step 2: 50 g/100 mL = x/1000 mL
x = 500 g
Step 3: 1 g dextrose/3.4 cal =
500 g dextrose/x
x = 1700 calories

59. b

2 g coal tar/60 g formula =
x/454 g formula
x = 15.1 g coal tar

60. b

Step 1: 1000 units/60 min. = x/1 min.
x = 16.67 units per minute
Step 2: 20,000 units/500 mL =
16.67 units/x
x = 0.42 mL per minute
Step 3: 15 gtt./1 mL = x/0.42 mL
x = 6.3 gtt. = 6 gtt./min.

61. d

Step 1: 40 g = 40,000 mg =
40,000,000 mcg
Step 2: 600 mcg/1 tab. =
40,000,000 mcg/x
x = 66,666 tablets

62. d

*Note: Because the diluent is **zero** percent, this problem can be worked several ways. The easiest method is by a simple dilution, i.e., (old volume) (old %) = (new volume) (new %). A second method is alligation alternate, but it requires additional work.*

(O.V.) (O.%) = (N.V.) (N.%)
(454 g) (20%) = (x) (5%)
x = 1816 g of 5%

63. c

Step 1: 0.25% = 0.25 g/100 mL = 250 mg/100 mL
Step 2: 250 mg/100 mL = x/15 mL
x = 37.5 mg
or
0.25% × 15 mL = 0.0375 g = 37.5 mg

64. a

Step 1: 5000 mL × 0.9% = 5000 × 0.009 = 45 g
Step 2: 2.25 g/1 tab. = 45 g/x
x = 20 tablets

65. c

Step 1: Total parts in this formula equal 15
1 + 6 + 8 = 15 parts
Step 2: 15 parts powder/1000 g = 6 parts/x
x = 400 g of calcium carbonate

66. c

Step 1: 5 mg/1 mL = 2.5 mg/x
x = 0.5 mL per dose
Step 2: 0.5 mL/1 dose = 10 mL/x
x = 20 doses

67. c

*Note: Diluent is **zero** percent so this can be solved by 2 methods.*
Step 1: (O.V.) (O.%) = (N.V.) (N.%)
(960 mL) (10%) = (x) (3%)
x = 3200 mL of 3% dilution made, but how much water must be added to the 960 mL?
Step 2: 3200 mL – 960 mL = 2240 mL of water added
or
Step 1: Alligation Alternate Method

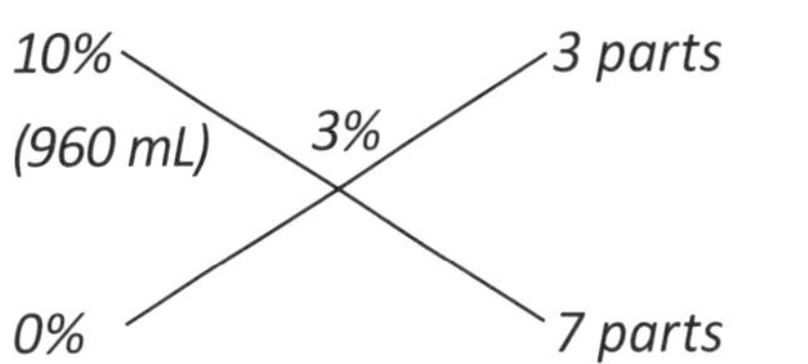

Step 2: 3 parts/960 mL = 7 parts/x
x = 2240 mL water

68. c

69. a

10 lb. = 4540 g = 4.54 kg
4.54 kg/340,000 tab. = x/170,000 tab.
x = 2.27 kg

70. d

71. a

50 mg/15 mL = x/960 mL
x = 3200 mg = 3.2 g

72. b

0.25 mg/1 tab. = x/50 tab.
x = 12.5 mg
65 mg/1 gr. = 12.5 mg/x
x = 0.192 gr.

73. b

74. b

80 mg/2 mL = 20 mg/x
x = 0.5 mL

75. c

18 gtt./1 mL = x/500 mL

x = 9000 gtt.

76. b

77. a

30 mg/1 m^2 = x/0.7 m^2

x = 21 mg

78. d

1 × 2 × 90 = 180

79. b

500 mcg/mL = 250 mcg/x

x = 0.5 mL

80. b

46/2.2 = 21 kg

4 mg/1 kg = x/21 kg

x = 84 mg

81. d

2 × 2 × 90 = 360

82. a

0.2 mg/15 mL = x/480 mL

x = 6.4 mg

83. b

8.8/2.2 = 4 kg

2.5 mg/1 kg = x/4 kg

x = 10 mg b.i.d. = 20 mg daily

84. c

85. a

1000 mL/480 min. = x/1 min.

x = 2.08 mL

86. a

12.5 mg/5 mL = x/960 mL

x = 2400 mg = 2.4 g

87. a

88. a

150 g/1000 tab. = x/50,000

x = 7500 g = 7.5 kg

89. d

250 g/1000 tab. = 2270 g/x

x = 9080 tablets

90. c

total weight of formula is 525.75 g

0.75/525.75 = 0.00143 = 0.143%

91. b

10 mL – 7.8 mL = 2.2 mL

92. c

100 mg/1 mL = 300 mg/x

x = 3 mL

93. a

100 mg/1 mL = x/10 mL

x = 1000 mg = 1 g

94. b

250 × 4 × 10 = 10,000 mg

1 g/1 vial = 10 g/x   x = 10 vials

95. b

2.2 + 9.8 = 12 mL per vial and it still contains 1000 mg of drug

1000 mg/12 mL = 250 mg/x

x = 3 mL

96. c

1000 mL/12 hr. = x/1 hr.

x = 83.3 mL

97. d

4,000,000 units/720 min. = x/1 min.

x = 5555 units

98. a

1000 mL/720 min. = x/1 min.

x = 1.39 mL/min.

99. d

1000 mL/12 hr. = x/1 hr.

x = 83.3 mL

15 gtt./1 mL = x/83.3 mL

x = 1250 gtt.

100. d

1 g benz./500 g oint. = x/120 g oint.

x = 0.24 g = 240 mg

101. c

5 g pre. sulf./100 g oint. = x/1000 g oint.

x = 50 g

102. c

103. b

Alligation Medial Method

1 kg × 10% = 10 kg%

+ 1 kg × 15% = 15 kg%

+ 1 kg × 20% = 20 kg%

---

3 kg 45 kg%

45 kg%/3 kg = 15%

104. c

(O.V.) (O.%) = (N.V.) (N.%)

(30 mL) (20%) = (1000 mL) (x)

x = 0.6%

105. d

0.6/100 = 1/x

x = 167 = 1:167

106. d

0.6 g/100 mL = x/15 mL

x = 0.09 g = 90 mg

107. b

108. d

Note: Using the alligation alternate technique, you will need 10 parts of 95% alcohol and 40 parts of 45% alcohol to make 50 parts of 55% alcohol.

109. b

50 parts/1000 mL = 10 parts/x

x = 200 mL of 95%

110. d

50 parts/1000 mL = 40 parts/x

x = 800 mL of 45%

111. b

10 parts/480 mL = 50 parts/x

x = 2400 mL of 55%

112. b

113. c

$14.88/12 = $1.24 (cost per tube)

$2.69 – $1.24 = $1.45 markup

114. c

$1.45/$2.69 = 0.54 = 54%

115. d

$1.45/$1.24 = 1.17 = 117%

116. c

$2.69 × 0.7 = $1.88

117. c

118. b

119. d

120. a

121. c

1200 cal/1000 mL = x/1500 mL

x = 1800 calories

122. d

43 g/1000 mL = x/60 mL

x = 2.6 g = 2600 mg

123. a

39 + 170 = 209 g/bottle

209 g/1 bottle = x/2 bottles

x = 418 g = 0.418 kg

124. d

2000 mg/1000 mL = 160 mg/x

x = 80 mL/hr.

125. d

10 g/1000 mL = x/15 mL

x = 0.15 g = 150 mg = 150,000 mcg

Appendix A

Updated Pharmacy Technician Certification Exam (PTCE) Blueprint Domains

The Pharmacy Technician Certification Board (PTCB) completed its most recent Job Analysis Study in February 2012. This analysis included information from over 25,000 pharmacy technicians across the United States. As outlined in **Section II** of this appendix, the PTCE domains have been updated to reflect the results of this analysis. For more information, visit the PTCB website at www.ptcb.org.

I. Previous PTCE Blueprint Functional Areas

Functional Areas	Functional Area Description	% of PTCE Content	Knowledge Statements
I	Assisting the Pharmacist in Serving Patients	66	84
II	Maintaining Medication and Inventory Control Systems	22	26
III	Participating in the Administration and Management of Pharmacy Practice	12	38

II. New PTCE Blueprint Domains

Knowledge Domains	Domain Description	% of PTCE Content	Knowledge Areas
1	Pharmacology for Technicians	13.75	6
2	Pharmacy Law and Regulations	12.5	15
3	Sterile and Nonsterile Compounding	8.75	7
4	Medication Safety	12.5	6
5	Pharmacy Quality Assurance	7.5	5
6	Medication Order Entry and Fill Process	17.5	7
7	Pharmacy Inventory Management	8.75	5
8	Pharmacy Billing and Reimbursement	8.75	5
9	Pharmacy Information Systems Usage and Application	10	2

Appendix B

Content Tested in Updated Pharmacy Technician Certification Exam (PTCE)[†]

I. Knowledge Domain 1: Pharmacology for Technicians (13.75% of exam)*

Exam Content	Chapter(s) in this book covering this content
Generic and brand names of pharmaceuticals	2
Therapeutic equivalence	1, 3, 7
Drug interactions (e.g., drug-disease, drug-drug, drug-dietary supplement, drug-OTC, drug-laboratory, drug-nutrient)	1, 7
Strengths/doses, dosage forms, physical appearance, routes of administration, and duration of drug therapy*	1, 6, 17
Common and severe side or adverse effects, allergies, and therapeutic contraindications associated with medications	2
Dosage and indication of legend, OTC medications, herbal and dietary supplements	2

II. Knowledge Domain 2: Pharmacy Law and Regulations (12.5% of exam)*

Exam Content	Chapter(s) in this book covering this content
Storage, handling, and disposal of hazardous substances and wastes (e.g., MSDS)	3, 9, 10, 12, 13
Hazardous substances exposure, prevention, and treatment (e.g., eyewash, spill kit, MSDS)	3, 9, 10, 13
Controlled substance documentation requirements for receiving, ordering, returning, transferring, loss/theft, and destruction (DEA)	3
Formula to verify the validity of a prescriber's DEA number (DEA)	7
Recordkeeping, documentation, and record retention (e.g., length of time prescriptions are maintained on file)	3, 6, 9, 10
Restricted drug programs and related prescription processing requirements (e.g., thalidomide, isotretinoin, clozapine)	4, 7
Professional standards related to data integrity, security, and confidentiality (e.g., HIPAA, backing up, and archiving)	3, 5
Requirements for consultation (e.g., OBRA-90)	3
FDA's recall classifications	13
Infection control standards (e.g., laminar air flow; clean room; hand washing; cleaning counting trays, countertop, and equipment) (OSHA, USP 795 and 797)	3, 9, 10
Recordkeeping for repackaged and recalled products and supplies (TJC, BOP)	3, 9, 10, 13
Professional standards regarding the roles and responsibilities of pharmacists, pharmacy technicians, and other pharmacy employees (TJC, BOP)	3
Facility, equipment, and supply requirements (e.g., space requirements, prescription file storage, cleanliness, reference materials) (TJC, USP, BOP)	3, 9, 10
State and federal laws and regulations	3, 13

III. Knowledge Domain 3: Sterile and Nonsterile Compounding (8.75% of exam)*

Exam Content	Chapter(s) in this book covering this content
Infection control (e.g., hand washing, PPE)	9, 10
Handling and disposal requirements (e.g., receptacles, waste streams)	3, 10, 12, 13
Determining product stability (e.g., beyond-use dating, signs of incompatibility)*	9, 10, 13
Selection and use of equipment and supplies	7, 9, 10, 12
Sterile compounding processes*	10, 15–18
Nonsterile compounding processes*	9, 15–18
Documentation (e.g., batch preparation, compounding record)*	9, 10, 12

IV. Knowledge Domain 4: Medication Safety (12.5% of exam)

Exam Content	Chapter(s) in this book covering this content
Error prevention strategies for data entry (e.g., giving prescription or medication order to correct patient)	6, 7, 11
Patient package insert and medication guide requirements (e.g., special directions and precautions)	4
Identifying issues that require pharmacist intervention (e.g., DUR, ADE, OTC recommendation, therapeutic substitution, misuse, missed dose)	7
Common safety strategies (e.g., tall man lettering, separating inventory, leading and trailing zeros, limiting use of error prone abbreviations)	11
Look-alike and sound-alike medications	11
High-alert medications	11

V. Knowledge Domain 5: Pharmacy Quality Assurance (7.5% of exam)

Exam Content	Chapter(s) in this book covering this content
Quality assurance practices for medication and inventory control systems (e.g., matching National Drug Code (NDC) numbers, bar codes, data entry)	7, 11–13
Risk management guidelines and regulations (e.g., error prevention strategies)	7, 12
Communication channels necessary to ensure appropriate follow-up and problem resolution (e.g., product recalls, shortages)	3, 5, 12, 13
Productivity, efficiency, and customer satisfaction measures	12
Infection control procedures and documentation	9, 10, 12

VI. Knowledge Domain 6: Medication Order Entry and Fill Process (17.5% of exam)*

Exam Content	Chapter(s) in this book covering this content
Intake, interpretation, data entry, and order entry processes*	5–7
Fill processes (e.g., select appropriate product, apply special handling requirements, measure product, and prepare product for final check)	7, 16–18
Labeling requirements (e.g., auxiliary and warning labels, expiration date, patient specific information)	7
Packaging requirements (e.g., type of bags, syringes, glass, pvc, child resistant, light resistant)*	7, 13
Dispensing processes (e.g., validation, documentation, and distribution)	7
Calculate doses required*	14–20

VII. Knowledge Domain 7: Pharmacy Inventory Management (8.75% of exam)*

Exam Content	Chapter(s) in this book covering this content
Function and application of NDC, lot numbers, and expiration dates	13
Formulary or approved/preferred product lists	7, 13
Ordering and receiving processes (e.g., maintaining par levels, rotating stock)*	13, 19
Storage requirements (e.g., refrigeration, freezer, warmer)	7, 9, 10, 13, 16
Product removal (e.g., recalls, returns, outdates, reverse distribution)	13

VIII. Knowledge Domain 8: Pharmacy Billing and Reimbursement (8.75% of exam)*

Exam Content	Chapter(s) in this book covering this content
Reimbursement policies and plans (e.g., HMOs, PPOs, CMS, private plans)	8, 19
Third-party resolution (e.g., prior authorization, rejected claims, plan limitations)*	8
Third-party reimbursement systems (e.g., PBM, medication assistance programs, coupons, and self-pay)	6–8, 19

IX. Knowledge Domain 9: Pharmacy Information Systems Usage and Application (10% of exam)

Exam Content	Chapter(s) in this book covering this content
Pharmacy-related computer applications for documenting the dispensing of prescriptions or medication orders (e.g., maintaining the electronic medical record, patient adherence, risk factors, alcohol drug use, drug allergies, side effects)	5–7
Databases, pharmacy computer applications, and documentation management (e.g., user access, drug database, interface, inventory reports, usage reports, override reports, diversion reports)	5

†Exam content based on best available knowledge from PTCB at the time of writing.

**Denotes content including calculations, according to PTCB (www.ptcb.org).*